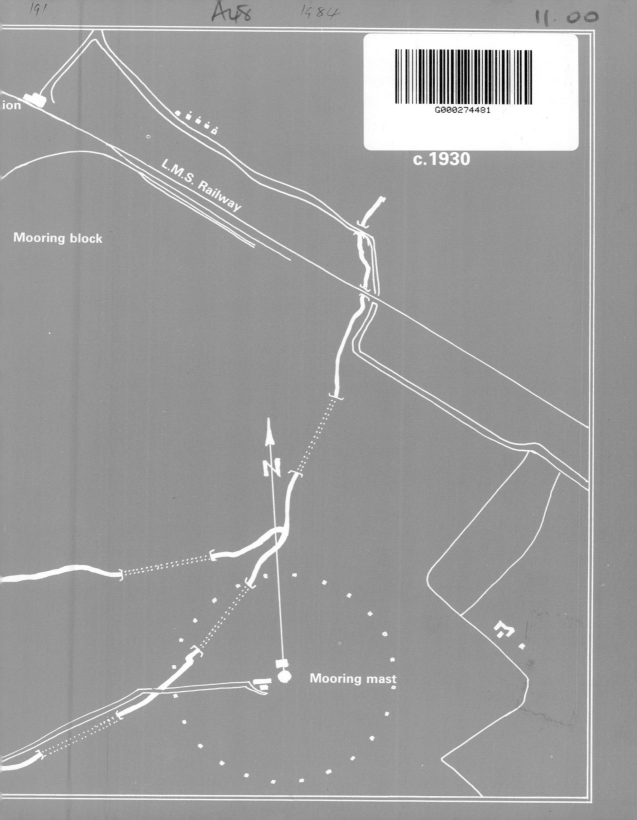

AIRSHIPS — CARDINGTON

AIRSHIPS — CARDINGTON

A history of Cardington airship station
and its role in world airship development

by

Geoffrey Chamberlain, A.M.R.Ae.S.

TERENCE DALTON LIMITED
LAVENHAM   .   SUFFOLK
1984

Published by
TERENCE DALTON LIMITED

ISBN 0 86138 025 8

Text photoset in 10/12 pt. Garamond

Printed in Great Britain at
The Lavenham Press Limited, Lavenham, Suffolk

Contents

Dedicated to the memory of
the late
Flight Sergeant G. W. Hunt, A.F.M. & Bar

Acknowledgements

Honouring my debts under this heading has become a daunting task because of the passage of time since the field research for this book began in 1969. By the time an edited manuscript was being made ready for the compositors I had already great cause to appreciate the support of my publishers, June and Terence Dalton. My very first responsibility, indeed, is to pay tribute to the effort put into this project by June Dalton, who died so suddenly and tragically at that particular time.

The retirement a few months later of editor John Venmore-Rowland only accentuated the loss, my work subsequently being in the hands of Robert Malster.

Writing now as a septuagenarian, I find myself confronted with the further sadness of discovering that so many of my past informers and advisers have also passed on. This in itself should not have caused me surprise, because in my self-imposed role of an entrepreneur striving to bridge the generation gap, I had been dealing with men who were essentially mature when I was still only a lad. All this makes it the more remarkable that I can now value the patronage of two great survivors of that heroic era who were makers of the history we are now examining herein.

The first is our foreword writer, Air Marshal Sir Victor Goddard, one of Admiral Fisher's original hand-picked naval airship captains. From the other side, so to speak, is the grand old Peter Morsdorf of Hamburg, now ninety-three and still hale and hearty despite his early trauma as the wireless operator of a German Zeppelin brought down in Britain in 1916.

Not all my encounters have been so rewarding or so glamorous; research work is much more of a routine, alleviated fortunately by the dedicated service of the many self-effacing curators, librarians and researchers of our national institutions, among which I record my gratitude to the Royal Aeronautical Society, the Public Record Office, the Science Museum, Cambridge University, the British Museum Newspaper Library, the National Physical Laboratory and other similar institutions.

Overseas organisations also have been especially helpful, experience of which began in 1973 with Kurt Puzicha in Hamburg when representing the Naval Zeppelin Comrades Association. A tour down through central Germany proved fruitful at many points, terminating at the shores of Lake Constance at the wonderful Zeppelin Museum in Friedrichshafen. Also in southern Germany, the most productive evidence of the Cardington connection was found in Mannheim where the original rival company to the Zeppelin organisation is still in existence. Here the principal directors, Herr Schneider and Herr Gensky, rendered assistance on an uprecedented scale. In Mannheim we were also grateful for the help of Dr. Ing. Langnickel, founder of a Zeppelin historic society and originally an engineering apprentice with the Count von Zeppelin. At Tubingen in the same region, the foundations were laid for three years of highly productive liaison with Kapitan Hans von Schiller, the last of the long-term officer captains of the Zeppelins.

Despite further intensive inquiries, it was not until 1983 by the courtesy of Wolfgang von Zeppelin that news was received of the death of Albert Sammt, one-time captain of LZ-130, the second *Graf Zeppelin*. The obscurity of his existence had doubtless been due to his own reputed modesty and to his having been a civilian employee of the Zeppelin company. He rose from being a helmsman to becoming a captain with Schiller himself. Fortunately, Wolfgang von Zeppelin had completed a biography of Sammt while he was still alive and we are grateful for having been able to embody certain information he supplied.

Another key information source came to light with the legacy of the personal archives of Professor Johannes Schutte being deposited with the "Landesmuseum für Technik und Arbeit" at Mannheim. Some two years of correspondence with this organisation resulted not only in the acquisition of valuable information but also the pleasure of receiving a visit in England from the keeper and researcher of the Schutte Archives, Dorothea Haaland, M.A. Dr Dieckerhoff of Wiesbaden is another historian who has made important data available to us by his prime investigations into the records of the German Army Zeppelin Battalions.

Researching in America was an especially pleasing experience within the limited time at my disposal, first at the Naval Air Technical Centre of the renowned Lakehurst airship station in New Jersey and later in the massive archives of the Smithsonian Institute at Washington. Also I recall with gratitude the very informative discussions I had in Peapack, N.J., with the late Willy von Meister, at one time Dr. Eckener's commercial representative in North America. He it was who gave me a first-hand account as a witness of the historic *Hindenburg* disaster. As a frequent passenger on the *Hindenburg* and the *Graf Zeppelin*, he was well qualified to answer my endless questions. It is regretted that the limitations of space have prevented me giving more than a superficial attention to the American airship scene, but that does not hinder me from giving praise to everyone over there who rendered such generous help.

In the international category, we have the American Goodyear Corporation who have contributed handsomely through their executives in three different countries, namely Mr Dick Sailer in Akron (Ohio), Mr R. Widdicombe (Rome), and Mr Christopher Aked (Wolverhampton). These people, by their connections with the *Europa* airship, bring us directly back to Cardington where she was first assembled and flown. For the earliest of all Cardington's history, we are most fortunate to have been guided by two of its founders, the late Claude Lipscomb, who was Chief Design Draughtsman for Shorts, and his deputy, the still surviving Harold Parker, residing in Amarillo, Texas. One other survivor of the Cardington of the First World War is the one-time naval architect Rex Andrew, of Bury St Edmunds. His overseer, H. A. Payne, died many years ago but once more we were fortunate to have acquired valuable information from papers inherited by his son Alan in

Australia. Both Payne and Andrew were contemporaries of Lieutenant-Commander A. P. Cole, M.B.E., who before he retired to Canada, where he died in 1975, had made some most important information available to us concerning the design of Britain's most successful airship, the R.33.

The mid-seventies was a depressing period, because of the losses sustained amongst important people of that generation. Captain George Meager, A.F.C., who had been First Officer of the R.100, made an enormous contribution before he died on 7th December, 1976. His counterpart in Germany, von Schiller, died on the very same day. Major-General Shotter, originally Chief Engineer on the famous transatlantic flight of the R.34, wrote me a seven-page account of his adventures only a month before he died in 1975 on the island of Sark; I had spent six years trying to trace him.

Among the riggers and the engineers were many old airshipmen with adventurous careers to recall, such as the late Billy Ballantyne who by his flight to America in the R.34 became the first stowaway in air history. Sid Duke from Tring still remembers sleeping in the keel of the R.29 while it made a bombing attack on a U-boat, while many more priceless anecdotes were gleaned during fascinating hours of chatting and drinking with the late Ted Stupple, Gerry Long, C. H. Rumsby, Fred Browdie and others of the Cardington, Pulham and Howden crews.

All six survivors of the R. 101 are now dead, but during their time I had known them all by sight. Some, like Cook, Bell and Binks, I knew rather better by virtue of having been welcomed in their homes during their last years. Binks was the last of them to go, in June, 1974. All of them have left their imprint within these pages, and we are grateful to them.

Most of the airship design personnel seem to have dispersed and become elusive, but fortunately again Mr L. A. Speed, a senior draughtsman on the R.101 team, has helped us enormously and, for good measure, the day spent in the company of the late Sir Barnes Wallis in his famous Brooklands office proved to be the most valuable of all the many wonderful occasions I have known of this kind; it was indeed a crash course on all the intricate problems of designing and building the R.100, as well as teaching a great deal about the notorious in-fighting that took place between the two major design teams of the age.

We are also indebted to Britain's greatest airship celebrity, Lord Ventry, who tells us in much detail how he and a few friends constructed a very small airship at Cardington more than thirty years ago and managed to crash it there! I last met this eighty-six-year-old warrior at Cardington, to where he had travelled laboriously with a broken ankle from Poole to indulge in a flight in the new British *Skyship 500*. How true it is that you can never keep a good man down!

We turn next to the subject of photographs, almost the mainstay of this volume, and express our thanks for the contributions made by Jim White of Shorts at Belfast, Mr N. A. Barfield and Mr Eric Morgan of British Aerospace at Weybridge, and Mr R. A. Forrester of Rolls Royce at Derby.

Of the many photographic collections examined over the years, it was inevitable that none could have been more rewarding than Cardington's own museum archives, so admirably administered by Frank Kiernan and his quietly efficient aide, Margaret Neaverson. On the other hand, some of our best individual items have emerged from quite small personal collections. Predictably, the most lucrative was that of the last rigid airship commander, Sir Victor Goddard. Several real gems came to light when I pursued some of my one-time school colleagues such as Albert Hunt, Sidney Burman, Don Beattie, Sid Miles, Jack Stevens, Jim Perkins and Margaret Chatterton. Most had fathers who had worked on the Cardington ships and some had also been crewmen. The late Squadron Leader Cook, who was Mast Officer at Cardington, left several previously unpublished photographs of great historic importance. His son David generously made these available, to very good effect. Diane Bayfield of the Great Yarmouth Central Library was particularly helpful in tracing rare pictures of the first Zeppelin raid. Moreover, no summary of this kind could omit to thank the many kindly acts of the staffs of our local newspapers with offices in Bedford, Barnet, Ipswich, Norwich, Great Yarmouth and Hull.

If only because our Cardington stories have ended with an updated description of the new *Skyship 500* and *600* projects being constructed and flown there, we are grateful to Lieutenant-Commander Ian Reid and Mr Bill Sedgwick, of Airship Industries Ltd. Their courtesy in giving access to these ships during the important stages of their construction was complemented by their readiness to discuss the technicalities implicit in the new constructional processes.

As I come now to the end of my efforts to thank all those who have made this work a possibility, I am conscious there must have been omissions and I therefore crave the indulgence of anyone in this category. My personal friend Alan Lloyd vetted my work daily for a year or more and I thank him for his kindly and unbiassed guidance on many occasions.

The editing of this book by John Venmore-Rowland before he retired, and latterly by Robert Malster, is a matter which has earned my especial appreciation, matched only by my gracious thanks to Terence Dalton, my publisher.

Ashford, Middlesex
January, 1984

Geoffrey Chamberlain

Foreword

by

Air Marshal Sir Victor Goddard, K.C.B., C. B.E.

This book is of great interest to me for reasons apparent to anyone reading this appraisal to the end, but what I really want to establish is the certainty that it will reward anyone—man, woman or child—who may have the good fortune to read it. It cannot fail to arouse the interest of them all, with its evidence of prolonged personal experience and patient, exciting and rewarding research.

Naturally, anyone able to remember the night-time rumbling of Zeppelin engines will read this book most avidly, whether or not such persons might also have heard the bombs being dropped by the Zeppelins, have seen the fires begun by their incendiaries, or even in certain rare instances have witnessed the actual destruction in flames of a raiding Zeppelin. In all such instances their readership can be taken for granted. Now however there is a much wider public, intent on the study of the early history of aerial bombardment which has brought western mankind at least to the recognition that "Thou Shalt Not Kill" is a valid prohibition. For until aerial bombardment began it had been expected that killing in war would be restricted to the armed forces.

That the rigid airship became notorious in its role as the original long-range bomber obscured its potential in other directions, and I am therefore pleased to recommend a study of this work to those of younger generations for whom very largely it has been written. After all, they are the people who in years to come will have the power to decide whether we as a nation, possibly even with the backing of other nations in Europe, should once more invest our efforts and resources in the development of the rigid airship principle.

Future rigid airships could well be even bigger than the giants of the past; simultaneously, prospects for the smaller non-rigid types of airship have probably never been more promising than they are today. Either way, an interim period of experimentation will be a certainty, whether on a national or international basis. That being so, Cardington by virtue of being the only rigid airship base remaining in Europe could well be regarded as likely for the construction of the airships still to come.

Thanks largely to the extensive coverage which this book has given to the development history of the rigid airship, we not only find it easier to see the significance of Cardington's early contributions but appreciate more clearly how its future could unfold yet again into a not too dissimilar pattern. In tracing the path of the earliest developments the author shows us how the courageous Count von Zeppelin originated the rigid airship in Germany and, after surmounting a whole decade of appalling difficulties, brought it to a viable level of efficiency. Having done so, the Count met with competition in Germany itself from a rival company called Schutte-Lanz.

The first two ships to be built at Cardington were in fact examples of the Schutte-Lanz type, being constructed with plywood instead of duralumin. How this change of policy came about makes fascinating reading, but the later rigid airships built at Cardington used duralumin and stainless steel.

It is fortunate for us today that there remains one who was born before the First

Air Marshal Sir Victor Goddard, President of the Airship Association, when he was a member of the Air Council in 1950.

World War in the Bedford district and who remembers a great deal of what went on among the airshipmen of Cardington. The author, to whom I refer, has applied himself to the task of reviving that history in remarkable detail and presenting it to us in so complete and enlightening a manner that we are left with the feeling that this must surely be unique.

In later years, the author travelled extensively in his searches to discover more about the airships of other nations. In particular he spent some useful time in

Germany, resulting in the physical retrieval of drawings and files, hidden away at the Schutte-Lanz works at Mannheim some sixty years previously, unknown to the directors of the present-day company. These drawings were examples of the great ships that we British copied during the war and afterwards.

When the First World War came to an end, Britain, France, Italy and America all received Zeppelins from Germany by way of reparations. It was during that period that America had been due to receive also the Cardington-built R.38, known to the Americans as the ZR-2. That failure and the Zeppelin *Hindenburg* disaster are both described in this book, as also is the construction of the ill-fated R.101 at Cardington. The author's description of the causes for the loss of that ship is intriguing, but perhaps not everyone will concur with his analysis of the disaster. Yet because he not only visited the scene of the crash but also studied the evidence given, he has at least brought new considerations into an old and much questioned verdict.

The author being a member of the Airship Association, of which body I happen to be the President, is clearly one who believes in the future of the airship when Civil Aviation ceases to be avid for speed and is more content to rely upon the gifts of nature. As Cayley, the Father of British Aeronautics, declared 180 years ago, "On a great scale, balloon floatage offers the most ready, efficient and safe means of aerial navigation." In like vein, the Count Zeppelin on his deathbed in 1917 and in distress about the use to which his life's work was being put, said "I may not live to see my ships coming into their own, but I am not anxious about the future. Airships are the predestined means for communciations between peoples of the earth."

How I came to have experience as captain of airships was being selected as a midshipman from a battleship in the Grand Fleet in March, 1915. The purpose was to combat in airships the submarine menace to our shipping. That led to my having flying experience in 1917 to 1921 with at least five of our Zeppelin types of airships and structural experience of several others, including the R.100 and R.101. That of course covered personal knowledge of the designers of the last two ships.

I count myself fortunate to be a witness of the revival of world interest in airships and to have been asked to write a Foreword for this important book.

Brasted,
March, 1981

Victor Goddard

Introduction

THE WORD Cardington is truly a world famous name, but though it is invariably used in an aeronautical context, it still has different meanings for different people. The function of this book is to make plain what those differences are.

First it should be seen that this name Cardington belongs by right to a small hamlet of some antiquity in a prosperous farming community, three miles south-east of the county town of Bedford. The "Cardington" generally referred to in an aviation sense is the scatter of airfield structures some two miles west of the village of Cardington. It has become almost a suburb of Bedford as the ever-expanding town continues to spread its tentacles further into the countryside.

Curious though it may seem to a stranger, local residents still speak of it as Shortstown, as has been customary for nearly seventy years; that is to say, ever since the Admiralty commissioned the world's first aircraft manufacturing company, the Short Brothers, to build "Zeppelins" for the Royal Navy. Even more curiously, archive material shows that Shorts letter headings of that period proclaim it to be

Cardington Naval Aircraft Works/Bedford

Within a relatively brief period, Shorts were ejected by compulsory purchase and the title of Royal Airship Works took over, thus confirming the original ambitions of the Admiralty policy makers who feared losing control to private industry. The identity of "Cardington" has been changed on several occasions since that time, the most modern one being

Ministry of Defence : Royal Aircraft Establishment : Cardington

By whatever name it may be remembered or whatever role it has served, the true charisma of Cardington is related unquestionably to the years of its original existence as an airship station. It was the last of the nine rigid airship stations to have been completed during the First World War, out of the score or more planned. It was one of the four to have come into being initially as construction bases, staffed by civilians. The remainder were purely operational and were manned by Naval personnel. Today, Cardington is the only remaining rigid airship station in the world out of all those constructed during the war, including more than fifty in German occupied territories.

We can be exceedingly thankful that Cardington remains virtually unchanged from its early airship days and is not only a unique symbol of our aeronautical heritage but also an inescapable reminder of a rare breed of aviation pioneers; clearly it is a great memorial.

Pondering on the history of this remarkable establishment, the writer long ago concluded that no mere diary of station events could be more than a parish record nor could it suffice to evaluate Cardington's role in global airship activities. No mere reference catalogue of four airships built and flown could depict the circumstances surrounding their conception, nor their effects on other nations similarly engaged. Not only do we need to examine the work of the other British airship stations to see why Cardington was so special, but also the activities of Germany, France, Italy and America must be considered if British proficiency (or lack of it!) is to be measured.

So far as the layman was concerned, the airship world at large might just as well have been a secret society, for all that filtered down to the level of Fleet Street in an age of wartime security and an impoverished media, impoverished, that is, in

British rigid-airship factories and bases 1908-1931

intellect. The result has been a legacy of legends and myths which have prospered and survived. The popular idea of life in the world of airships was, at the best, sketchy—while at the opposite end of the spectrum it has become universally ludicrous.

The realities, of course, were different. One particular aspect stands out with clarity and significance; so intense and so constant was the cross-fertilisation of ideas, in some cases by legitimate and legal exchange and in others by espionage, that no part of airship history can be studied in isolation with an adequate comprehension.

It is an axiom that the entire forty years history of the giant rigid airship is one whole saga in its own right, and the many attempts made by historians to dissect and dismember its numerous parts have seldom met with satisfaction. Logically, it makes

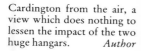
Cardington from the air, a view which does nothing to lessen the impact of the two huge hangars. *Author*

sense to open up for detailed examination the specific area or sector of interest for special attention, but only when it is viewed in the perspective of contemporary activity can the discoveries made be properly assessed.

Entirely within this context, it is fully justifiable to produce a new book that can emphasise the novel disclosures we are about to impart concerning Cardington but not at the expense of neglecting the greater backcloth. It was an era that began with the first German Zeppelin in 1900, even before the Wright Brothers had flown.

As the century draws to its close and airship activity focusses once more upon Europe's only surviving complex, the time is ripe for us to take stock of this rather special district bearing the illustrious name of Cardington, the district which the author is proud to claim as his birthplace, together with three generations before him.

CHAPTER ONE

Shorts' Story

O N SATURDAY, 30th April, 1977, The Royal Aircraft Establishment at
Cardington, Bedfordshire, was open to the public to celebrate the sixtieth
anniversary of what most people supposed was the opening of the Royal Air Force's
Royal Airship Works in 1917. This was not so, however, since neither the Royal Air
Force nor the Royal Airship Works existed in 1917. Rather was it to celebrate the
opening of the Cardington Naval Aircraft Works of the world's first aircraft
manufacturing company, Short Brothers of Rochester.

The original Cardington factory was not entirely Ministry owned but a
legitimate branch of the Short Brothers company. It was built for Shorts with money
borrowed from the government and came into existence solely to meet a government
requirement.

It is not clear who selected the Cardington site, but obviously it was well
chosen, since in the Great Ouse Valley the land was cheap and clear of obstacles and
severe winds. Road and rail communications were good and the labour supply
plentiful. Another asset was its nearness to London, an hour by train, enabling Shorts
to maintain an excellent and rapid liaison with the Admiralty. The same could hardly
be said for other manufacturers in the airship industry who were located as far away
as Barrow-in-Furness and Glasgow.

Why was another airship manufacturing base needed? Examination of that
question reveals a most intriguing situation.

Naval movements during the First World War were attended by great anxiety
because of our absence of air cover. Unquestionably our capacity for sustaining the
war at sea was achieved only by the slenderest of margins; the British Isles were in
very real danger of coming under threat of siege and starvation if we once lost control
of affairs in home waters. The submarine and the torpedo had become the really big
menace at sea.

None of this occasioned any surprise whatever to Admiral Lord (John) Fisher of
Kilverstone, who from the turn of the century had made it his sole function in life to
upgrade the Royal Navy into a sophisticated weapon capable of facing all the
challenges of the twentieth century. He made enemies but also found allies; usually
men who were younger and in general more receptive to progress and to change.
Among these was Captain (later Admiral) R. H. S. Bacon, knowledgeable and

Cardington on 6th November, 1918, with R.31
circling the works before leaving. The bows of R.32
can be seen in the hangar doorway. *H. G. Parker*

1

anxious to introduce airships for service at sea with the fleet. It was almost entirely due to continuous lobbying by Bacon among endless committees and sub-committees that a general sanction to set up an experimental airship programme for the Royal Navy was granted in 1908.

No aircraft industry existed, and in 1908 nobody had yet flown an aeroplane in Great Britain. The Englishman Henry Farman had made the first recorded flights in France and others were on the point of making France virtually the birthplace of aviation in Europe. In Britain, there were few visible signs of activity, but this was to change very rapidly. There was no obvious simple course for an organisation wanting to build something as novel, complicated and enormous as the German Zeppelin already flying with reasonable success over Lake Constance, though there were Royal Engineers at Farnborough experimenting with a motorised balloon, the *Nulli Secundus*, but not achieving very much success.

Those in the Admiralty who were the proponents of the big rigid airship were few in number and with no resources of the right kind at their disposal. They eventually turned to Vickers for the solution to their problems, because that company was the principal supplier of war materials to the Admiralty. Involved was the Submarine Division of Vickers operating alongside the Cavendish Dock at Barrow-in-Furness, there being positively no connection with the well-known aircraft division of Vickers-Armstrongs that later flourished for so many years at Weybridge. The choice of boiler-plate engineers to construct an airship is at least surprising.

In that same August of 1908 when Vickers had been invited to tender for the contract for Britain's first rigid airship, the celebrated Wright Brothers had made their first flights in Europe; Wilbur had made his first flight of 105 seconds at Le Mans. Eustace and Oswald Short had been in the balloon manufacturing business for ten years at Hove, near Brighton, displaying considerable initiative in the process.

The station is thrown open to the public on 30th April, 1977, regarded as the sixtieth anniversary of the opening of Cardington. *Author*

Their catalogue for 1902 was remarkable in that it offered "to construct flying machines and kites, etc., from plans and to conduct aeronautical experiments".

By 1902 they had already designed a pressurised capsule for high-altitude balloon ascents and in the following year they received orders from the Government of India for military observation balloons. During the next few years they moved from Hove to London, taking up residence first in an old carriage shed in London Mews off the Tottenham Court Road and later in the railway arches at Battersea. By 1907 Eustace and Oswald had been appointed Aeronauts to the Aero Club, not yet having the title "Royal", and by September, 1908, they had become convinced that the ballooning days were numbered and announced their firm intention of turning over their factory to the manufacture of aeroplanes. By March, 1909, Shorts had already contracted to build six aeroplanes for the Wright Brothers in a brand-new factory on the Isle of Sheppey.

As the world's first aircraft manufacturer, having also had lengthy experience in the lighter-than-air field, one might have expected this company to have been enlisted immediately for the design and construction of Britain's first rigid. It could have been merely coincidence that the contract went to Vickers at the same time that Shorts came to terms with the Wright Brothers, but it is not too difficult to sense a degree of enthusiasm on the part of Shorts sufficient to have made them reluctant to divert into the airship business on such a scale just as they were embarking on what may have seemed like the adventure of a lifetime.

However, they were brought into the picture in due course as the contributors of gas-cells and of the envelope and of various ancillary components. A further seven years would elapse before Shorts came into airship construction as fully commissioned designers and builders.

Not surprisingly, the story does not begin in Cardington, since the nucleus of the original team had assembled for the first time at a private house in Ranulf Road, Hampstead, in the spring of 1916. By September the unit had transferred to Bedford. In 1916 Bedford was a prosperous little market town with a sufficiency of high-grade light engineering works and a population of about 35,000. Outside the town, to the north-east at Putnoe, now an integral part of Bedford, was a handsome stretch of farmland which served as an aerodrome for the Royal Flying Corps, part of the United Kingdom defence network against the Zeppelins that were causing so great a disturbance at that time. Within sight of and opposite to Putnoe was, and still is, the village of Cardington proper. With only a few hundred inhabitants, it remains as ever physically removed from the air station some two miles to the west.

It is strange testimony to the quirks of history that the establishment known all over the world by the name of Cardington is still better known to the local population by the name of the company that founded it originally. To visit the establishment one looks for signs to Shortstown, not Cardington. The registered title of the parent company became Short Brothers (Rochester & Bedford) Limited. The title states Bedford, not Cardington, and it remained this way not only during Shorts' four years' occupancy of the Cardington premises but for many years afterwards until the company moved to Belfast and became Short & Harland Limited. In more recent times it has reverted to something closer to the original and is now known quite simply as Shorts Limited.

The accent on Bedford, rather than Cardington, stems from the original need of the company to get its design section operational without having to wait for the vast Cardington factory complex to be built. The problem was easily resolved by renting the upper storey of a local coach repair premises known as Nicholl's Garage at a point opposite St Mary's Church, to the south of the Bedford Town Bridge. The man who headed this enterprise was the twenty-nine-year-old Claude Lipscomb, who had originally served an apprenticeship at Woolwich Arsenal but had joined Shorts at the outbreak of war in 1914, attracted by the prospect of technological adventuring extended by the new aviation world. Few then realised that the shy, retiring young Lipscomb was destined to spend the rest of his working life with Shorts, ultimately to retire as Technical Director several years after the Second World War. Most of the endless sequence of successful aircraft emerging from Shorts' factories on the Medway and in Belfast evolved under his supervision.

He set up his first drawing loft in Bedford in September, 1916. Not only will this date be seen as the genesis of Cardington's own extensive history but it was also the

Young Claude Lipscomb on the roof of the Cardington drawing office in 1918.   *H. G. Parker*

Shorts set up their drawing office in 1916 in the attic of the coach repair shop seen in the left-hand corner of this view of the crossroads about 200 yards south of Bedford's river bridge.　　*H. G. Parker*

very month when the rigid airship as a species incurred the greatest setback in the whole of its forty-year history, a phase that one could perhaps refer to as "The First Battle of Britain".

That September, four of Germany's newest two-million-cubic-feet monsters became mere heaps of smouldering ash in the fields of the Home Counties. From this time on, Britain's defence network paid handsome dividends. As long-range aeroplanes took over from the Zeppelins, our improving techniques and equipment did much more to counter this new mode of attack. In the opinion of most military people in Germany, the Zeppelin had become a bitter disappointment and should be finished with. Today, few would argue with that, but how did it seem in Britain in the autumn of 1916?

If Germany had lost the initiative with the super-Zeppelin weapon, despite her massive background of experience, then it was insanity for Britain to think she could do any better. Despite the alarm bells which rang loud and clear, the development of large rigid airships was being permitted to go ahead at Bedford and Cardington as though nothing whatever had happened.

Adding to the mystification was the question of our ability to build similar ships, since Britain had been engaged on the idea, on and off, since 1908 and still had

The first hangar at Cardington under construction in September, 1916.

not succeeded in getting one into the air. This was not altogether the fault of the airship builders themselves, but even so Vickers had been involved for most of this period and Beardmore and Armstrong Whitworth had also joined in some time after the war began.

Yet here were Shorts about to set up their drawing boards, and the word "expensive" was being applied in its broadest context, for we were about to deprive the wartime aircraft industry of a number of talented young designers and artisans. There was the drain on our wartime resources for building the massive factory complex of Cardington; it nearly required an Act of Parliament to release the thousands of tons of steel needed for the hangar alone. The shed, or hangar, was the biggest to be erected in Britain up to that time and its need to provide a minimum space for two ships under one cantilever roof resulted in an internal width of 180 feet. The internal length of 700 feet and height of 110 feet ensured that it would be possible to build ships that would in no way be inferior in size to the biggest Zeppelins constructed up to that time.

One of the refinements to this hangar, and a further consumer of steel, was the provision of enormous windbreaks at both ends, it being possible to move a ship in or out of either end. As long as the shed itself, these windscreens were designed to protect an airship during the whole of the time it was being manoeuvred into or out of the shed. It was customary to paint a sequence of numbers along the length of the screen; as the airship slowly moved along the ground, the occupants of the control-car, reading the numbers exactly opposite them on the screen, knew the distance in feet to the hangar door, thus the extent to which the ship was or was not clear of this notoriously hazardous obstacle.

So far as it was practical to do so, the entire undertaking was intended to be self-sufficient. For a start, there was the really substantial permanent design and administration block constructed at the top of the slope overlooking the aerodrome and hangar site proper, while behind it was, and still is, the orderly array of orthodox manufacturing workshops needed for girder construction. Among them was the large glass-roofed "Arcade", with its all-important humidity and temperature control, for the construction and testing of gas-cells, and finally the actual gasworks where the hydrogen needed was generated by a method which involved the passing of steam over scrap iron in a heated retort.

There were numerous ancillary services and back-up facilities such as the engine test-beds, the motor transport depot, the sewerage works and so on, until one is amazed at the sheer scale of the exercise. Then there was the complete housing estate that had to be built on the opposite side of the road to accommodate the workforce and their families.

Having demonstrated our ability to destroy the most sophisticated of German airships, even under cover of darkness, why was it that Britain continued to develop the identical type of aircraft to the utmost of her limited resources? Even the possiblity of the war ending was not allowed to interfere with this ponderous programme; it was obvious that it could be two years before an end-product emerged at Cardington.

The first ship to come out of Cardington, the R.31, was commissioned only five days before the Armistice of 11th November, 1918, and two years and two months from the time when Lipscomb had set up in Bedford. The gestation period of over two years was not surprising, and it would be unrealistic to compare the situation at Cardington with the contemporary high rate of output of the German Zeppelins, which had been coming out of at least eight factories, if one includes the Schutte-Lanz factories, at a rate of one every six weeks.

Against such a background, the Cardington achievement must truly be assessed as commendable. The challenge as seen by young Lipscomb in 1916 was surely a daunting one, and it was only too apparent that a great gamble was being taken. The general public, having seen the succession of Zeppelin catastrophes in that fateful September, must have been baffled as to what we were hoping to do with similar vessels. That the hydrogen-filled rigid was a poor military weapon was manifest already to the Germany Army who, with their own independent Zeppelin Force, were at that time carefully assessing the costs. The survey led to disbandment of the Force within a few months. The German Admiralty was also losing its earlier confidence but pressed on, albeit reluctantly.

The fact that there were two independent Zeppelin Forces existing in Germany is often a source of surprise, but it is this very aspect of Zeppelin utilisation which offers the clue as to which of Britain's armed services had need of a Zeppelin equivalent, and why. The Royal Flying Corps had neither an interest nor an involvement, which was why the British rigid airship was not adopted for battlefield reconnaissances or for long-range bombing, as had largely been the case with its German counterpart.

The responsibility for manning British airships fell to the Royal Naval Air Service, and the functions they were to perform were at the discretion of and under the control of the Admiralty. The command and administration of such operations are the most natural and proper of Admiralty functions, but when it comes to the actual provisioning of the weapons of war, matters enter a bureaucratic and political jungle. Cardington, as a facility, was initially only the final small sector of a far greater overall programme of rigid airship construction in Britain.

With three major companies already committed to producing more than a dozen big ships, somehow Cardington got caught up in the momentum of an undertaking so vast that, once started, it was not easy to stop. Possibly the most intriguing thing to come out of all this was the manner in which the actual purpose and functional role of Cardington changed in its earliest times and so set it uniquely apart from the rest. Originally it had been planned by the Admiralty for Shorts to provide what would be nothing more than an extra assembly line as an extension to Beardmore and Armstrong Whitworth, who themselves were already tied to Vickers as the accepted design authority. The impact of this latter may be fully apparent only to one who is a qualified engineer; for others it can be emphasised that the Admiralty, having to accept that both the expertise and basic technical control of naval airship development was in the hands of a commercial organisation, found itself in an untenable situation.

This situation had prevailed ever since Vickers became involved, quite legally and contractually, in the design and construction of Britain's first rigid, H.M.A. No. 1, better known as *Mayfly*, in 1908.

With the active connivance of sections of the Admiralty, everything and anything that could be learned about the German airships eventually found its way into the Vickers design offices. There was no way the Admiralty could reverse the process or hold back vital information from Vickers, irrespective of how it had been obtained; thus despite the ambitions of senior naval staff to exert the maximum technical control over the construction of their own ships, nothing had been achieved in this way by 1916 except that the magic phrase Royal Airship Works had at last crept into their vocabulary and their thinking. It was in this atmosphere that the concept of a Cardington establishment dedicated to independent design and development was born.

Such an eventuality had not escaped the attention of Oswald Short, and in trying to anticipate it he came up with a very advanced design of his own, to have a two million cubic feet capacity and a designed top speed of 70 m.p.h. It had been no secret for quite a time that the Admiralty wanted to get full control, yet the brothers Short were sincere in their belief that they could offer a superior alternative. In a letter to the author in 1970, the late Claude Lipscomb expressed the opinion that the design offered by Shorts really did have merit to a high degree. Oswald Short was made to understand that the wartime function of Shorts' new Cardington team would be to interpret Admiralty specifications and to provide the detail design and constructional services required, under direct Admiralty supervision. In brief, the Admiralty would determine what was wanted and it was up to Shorts to produce it. Surprisingly, it does seem to have worked fairly well; it has been possible to verify from survivors of that era that both parties held a healthy respect for each other and a basic harmony prevailed.

Although there is little doubt that Oswald Short accurately judged the limited extent of airship technology within the Admiralty, he was not aware until afterwards that the Admiralty held a trump card relieving them of a need to look to Shorts for a

Oswald Short. *Shorts Ltd.*

total design. There existed at Mannheim during the First World War a most worthy and competent rival to the Zeppelin company called Schutte-Lanz. Unknown to anyone in Shorts, an employee of the Schutte-Lanz company had absconded to Britain in 1915, complete with plans of the S.L. airships and a knowledge of their novel manufacturing techniques and processes.

Since this company had been in direct competition with the Zeppelin concern it was natural that there were fundamental differences in the designs of the two companies. Its founder had been the eminent Professor Johannes Schutte, a highly trained naval architect from the University of Danzig and at one time an ardent supporter of Count von Zeppelin. Unfortunately their relationship deteriorated and in 1910 they went their separate ways, the Count pressing on stolidly with the conservative but reliable ideas of his own chief designer, Ludwig Durr, while Schutte secured the commercial backing of Karl Lanz and with him set up the company which, although it has not built airships for over sixty years, is still a thriving and highly respected organisation today.

Though the basics of the Zeppelin designs had become fairly well known to British designers by this time, the Schutte-Lanz system had remained relatively unknown, and it was this that had dropped like a ripe plum into the Admiralty's lap with the arrival in Britain of the defector from Mannheim, a matter which was kept secret from Shorts. Lipscomb's deputy, Mr H. G. Parker, now residing in Texas, was adamant that he was quite unaware of this until enlightened by the author around 1970. In some respects, the S.L. designs were undoubtedly superior to the now traditional Zeppelin structures, but this was of less importance to the Admiralty than the reality that they were different. It could hardly have suited the Admiralty better, because their acquisition of S.L. technology severed their dependence on Vickers and removed the source of irritation which had also plagued their other earlier connection with Vickers in respect of submarines. Not only had the Admiralty retrieved an embarrassing situation but it had advanced the state of the art beyond that achieved by Vickers at Barrow.

Oswald Short was robbed of the chance to put his own design theories to the test, but he no longer faced the alternative of becoming a mere sub-contractor to Vickers. Suddenly he found his own company way out in front in terms of political status and patronage, having become the chosen instrument of Admiralty policy.

When Lipscomb began drafting detail designs in the attic of Nicholl's Garage, he was already using outline drawings sent to him from Smith Square, Westminster; the nucleus of an Admiralty design team as originally envisaged by the great Murray Sueter was already being formed from a few well-chosen personnel of the Royal Corps of Naval Constructors. Under the direction of Commander C. I. R. Campbell, a new silent service, devoid of a public identity, began steadily to take on more and more tasks relating to the design and inspection of rigid airships, so that by the end of the war its influence was considerable.

CHAPTER TWO

Origin of the Species

FRIEDRICHSHAFEN, on the northern shores of Lake Constance, was the birthplace of the rigid airship; here the visitor is certain to discover nearly everything he may need to know concerning the origins of the rigid airship.

This splendid town of some 60,000 inhabitants is steeped in the history of the ancient kings of the German states and is the epicentre of world airship history, and the post-war Zeppelin Museum is both a memorial to a great man and a fascinating treasure-house of mementoes and of information. It perpetuates the name of Count Ferdinand von Zeppelin, who made Friedrichshafen the base for his work right from the beginning. The Count was born in the city of Constance, at the south-western extremity of the lake of the same name, on 8th July, 1838. He came of a long line of Württemberg aristocracy and a French mother, Amalia Macaire D'Hogguer. He spent his life up to the age of fifty-two as a military man, his last command before retirement being that of a brigade of Prussian cavalry.

From the time he left the Army to the time his first creation took to the air on 2nd July, 1900, was a complete decade. The fact that this memorable date was a full three years before the Wright Brothers in America made their first aeroplane flights makes us realise the almost complete absence of empirical data for the Zeppelin team to work on for the world's first big rigid airship. The fact that it flew at the first attempt, albeit for only eighteen minutes, and also the fact that its test pilot was none other than the sixty-two-year-old ex-cavalry commander, is sufficient to demonstrate that the entire concept was in the hands of an extremely forceful and dedicated man, however stubborn he may have appeared to the journalists of the day.

If he had a secret at all, it was his inborn talent for spotting talent in others and an indisputable flair for welding competent individuals into a team. Karl Maybach and Claudius Dornier were among his early proteges and, like Hugo Eckener, the greatest father-figure to the airship world at large, they owed their ultimate eminence to the early direction of their careers by the Count von Zeppelin.

The outside professional engineer responsible for the fundamental structural layout forming the basic principle of all Zeppelin's airships, Müller-Breslau, afterwards faded right out of the Zeppelin picture. The system he devised and brought into being was simply that of a series of near-circular formers of girder construction, secured and spaced apart by a convenient number of horizontal girders, the whole assembly closely resembling a giant cigar in profile. Balloons containing hydrogen were accommodated within the length of the structure like so many peas in a pod, the casing of the pod in this instance being the light-weight fabric which served to maintain the chosen overall shape of the airship, regardless of the constantly changing shapes of the gas balloons under the influence of altitude changes.

This history-making first Zeppelin rigid airship was quite a monster by comparison with contemporary non-rigids, being 420 feet long and 38 feet in diameter. The LZ-1, as it was known, took some two years to build. The gas-cells were made from a rubberised cotton fabric at Augsburg and the Daimler motor company provided the two 16 h.p. petrol engines, each of which was installed in its own engine-car and drove its own pair of pylon-mounted four-bladed metal propellers. The engine-cars were open to the elements and looked like boats, which effectively they were, so that the entire vessel could float on water, a feature which remained common to Zeppelin rigids for many years after and was probably the

Count Ferdinand von Zeppelin, as viewed by the British technical press in 1910.

reason why the cars became generally known as "gondolas" (a term which still holds good in American airship jargon).

Whether we call them power-cars, engine-cars or gondolas, their function is unmistakeable. In the original Zeppelin such units were attached rigidly to the airframe structure at about a quarter of its length from either end and were joined together by a single aluminium girder which served as a rail, along which a 2 cwt. lead weight could be hand-winched to achieve fore and aft trimming in flight.

Among the secondary features of this essentially experimental ship was the provision of signal bells and telephones for communication between the cars. Only a single helm wheel was fitted, since unlike all its successors, the LZ-1 was equipped only with directional rudders and not with elevators, the sliding weight being considered not only adequate but even superior since its effect on the climb or dive attitude was not dependent on having powerful slipstream over the aerofoil surfaces.

It would be an exaggeration to suggest that the whole thing was bristling with bright ideas, but nevertheless there was an impressive logical handling of the novel demands being made on the creators of this great project. Typical was the assembly hangar, which was quite simply a huge floating barn, swinging at its moorings offshore from Manzell, near Friedrichshafen. The arrangement was intended to give the secrecy of an island factory and also to ensure that the ability of the shed to head into the wind should eliminate the danger of side winds as a ship entered or emerged from its shed, the very problem that was to plague all Zeppelin crews in the years ahead.

The late Ernst Lehmann, commander of the ill-fated *Hindenburg*, tells us that:

"the float on which the airship rested was pushed from the hangar . . . and outside on the lake, the little steamer *Buckhorn* took the strange monster in tow and pulled it against the wind. A screen protected the smoke-stack of the tugboat so that no sparks could reach

Dr Ludwig Durr, chief designer of Zeppelin airships.　*Kurt Puzicha*

the floating airship . . . when the airship had climbed high enough on the towrope and the motors had begun to turn . . . the speed was not great, the motorboat easily held pace with it . . . but what could be expected of the two Daimler marine motors which at 800 revs developed an average of 24 and a maximum of 32 horse-power? Historians should bear that in mind and not only record that the flight lasted but eighteen minutes but that the airship was forced to land on the water near Immenstaad because the sliding weight lever had broken, the ship's hull had buckled and the rudder ropes had become tangled."

Repairs were carried out and two more flights were made in October, 1900, before the company ground to a halt as the Count's personal finances expired.

The floating hangar was brought ashore and the ship dismantled; with the exception of one young engineer, everybody else was discharged. The Count entered into a wilderness of crusading that was to last for another five years.

With von Zeppelin working constantly to keep the whole exercise alive, it fell to his disciples to interpret his ideas and translate them into the realities of flight. Undoubtedly the greatest of these, yet the least known, was the solitary youth who had been kept on the payroll after the rundown of the original team in the autumn of

1900, when LZ-1 had been dismantled and the lessons of her flight history had still to be evaluated. This was Ludwig Durr, who had joined the company as a twenty-one-year-old fitter-mechanic on the LZ-1 and thereafter stayed with the organisation for the rest of his life, despite several tempting offers from America. Durr was responsible for all the subsequent 118 Zeppelins built.

Durr slid very naturally and effectively into the Technical Director's chair, but there was another man who also came quite early into the Zeppelin picture, Dr Hugo Eckener, one-time law student and freelance press reporter. He came on to the Zeppelin scene because he was living near Friedrichshafen at the time when the *Frankfurter-Zeitung* wanted someone local to report on the activities of the Count. The connection thus arrived at was the catalyst that made Eckener the ultimate successor to the Count; as events were to demonstrate and history was to record, Hugo Eckener would rule the Zeppelin empire and simultaneously become the greatly loved and respected maestro of the rigid airship world.

With plenty of time but no money to spare, young Ludwig Durr systematically isolated each aspect of the design of the prototype Zeppelin and upgraded the original integrity of it by every means at his disposal, which included Europe's first aeronautical wind-tunnel, designed and built by Durr from surplus materials. One of the most important changes achieved was Durr's rejection of the "T" and "I" section aluminium girders used in the skeleton of the LZ-1. In their place he evolved a method of building girder units from lengths of thin rolled strip, dimpled and channelled to give it far greater strength. When all-metal aeroplanes came into use years later Durr's method became the standard for aircraft builders all over the world.

Durr replaced the two 16 h.p. Daimler engines with the much-improved 85 h.p. ones. Elevators were installed for the first time and the sliding ballast weight was rejected, but overall the major dimensions remained the same as before.

On 17th January, 1906, this second ship took off, with results that were little short of disastrous. The ascent was excessively rapid, certain engine accessories caused both engines to fail, and finally the wind snatched the vessel away from the lake and, virtually out of control, LZ-2 went off across country for twenty miles before she could be brought down to a safe landing. Overnight, the wind which had caused most of the trouble became progressively worse, finally wrecking the moored ship beyond any hope of repair.

The indomitable spirit of the sixty-eight-year-old Count fought back, and it was at this stage that Eckener, though as yet not in any way in the employ of von Zeppelin, became emotionally involved by being witness to the Count's dedication. Eckener became a self-appointed campaigner and was so successful in capturing public support for the Zeppelin cause that a charitable lottery floated the company back into business in an astonishingly short time.

Within the year a third and now really flyable Zeppelin took to the air. Launched on 9th October, 1906, LZ-3 was a success from the start and good fortune followed this "lucky ship" for the following seven years. Flights of several hours' duration were frequently and safely accomplished, due very largely to the attention that had been paid by Ludwig Durr to the twin problems of stability and control. In retrospect, there is much to be said for seeing LZ-3 as the world's first really practical airship; certainly it was in the ensuing year of 1907 that public approbation was completely won for the first time and, more importantly, it was also the year when the German Government displayed the first signs of serious interest; they actually promised financial support if certain specified advances in performance could be achieved. Clearly this was all the stimulus needed to rationalise affairs, create a substantial new company and build another new ship, the fourth.

When completed in June, 1908, LZ-4 showed that progress was indeed being maintained. Quite apart from a variety of minor innovations, the ship was the first to provide passenger accommodation in a completely separate compartment amidships.

During the summer of 1908, the LZ-4 logged a record number of flying hours and its many flights in those couple of months were outstandingly successful. National pride, stirred by the achievements of LZ-3, received a further boost from the dramatic long-distance day and night flights of LZ-4 in the competent hands of Ludwig Durr and von Zeppelin himself. A forced landing in darkness due to engine trouble on the night of 4th August was accomplished successfully, but their luck deserted them yet again. The ship was picketed down firmly in open countryside not far from Stuttgart when a summer storm wrenched the enormous hull from its moorings and scattered it across the landscape in a spectacular blazing tangle of wreckage. Undeterred, the amazing old von Zeppelin immediately let it be known that he intended to press on as before, once he could sort out his precarious finances. German society reacted in a fantastic wave of sentiment and a torrent of donations descended on Friedrichshafen.

As the newest ship, LZ-5, began taking shape, the old LZ-3 had been modified and refurbished and had made history of a kind by being purchased by the German Army for evaluation purposes, receiving the new identity Z-1 in the process. New construction sheds had been set up, this time on dry ground on the outskirts of Friedrichshafen, and LZ-6 was already being planned.

Two other events taking place that year can now be seen to have been the most influential occurrences to affect all subsequent Zeppelin history. One was the appointment of Hugo Eckener to the permanent staff of the Zeppelin company, contrary to his own inclinations, and the other the formation of a sister company solely for creating a market for civilian air travel in ships to be built for the purpose by the Zeppelin construction company. Known colloquially as "DELAG", from the initials of the title Deutsche Luftschiffahrts Aktien Gesellschaft (German Airship Transport Company), it was founded in Frankfurt on 16th November, 1909.

At that time, the British press was carrying the story of the historic first mile flown in a British aeroplane by a British pilot, Mr Moore (later Lord) Brabazon. Barely four months previously, Bleriot's aeroplane crossing of the English Channel had similarly captured the headlines. A news item which passed unnoticed concerned growing anxiety in the Committee of Imperial Defence at the prospect of war with Germany and of the threat that might be posed by the development of the Zeppelin airship at Friedrichshafen. In 1909, the first British Zeppelin was being designed by the Vickers Maxim Company of Barrow-in-Furness.

Like most commercial managers of risky enterprises, Alfred Colsmann of the Zeppelin company doubtless had qualms in launching Delag, but if he needed proof of the nation's continued moral support, he had only to remember the tumultuous welcome accorded to the Count and to Eckener in August when they flew the LZ-6 into Tegel, near Berlin. There they were received by Emperor Wilhelm himself. Colsmann was tough and well aware that if they had to wait for the German ministries to fill the order book his company would soon be in the hands of the receiver. Acting swiftly while popular support was still high, Colsmann, aided and abetted by Eckener, skilfully solicited the burgomasters of the greater cities of Germany and, winning the support of the majority, succeeded in getting a number of well separated sites organised as proper landing grounds, some of them complete with big hangars for maintenance and operational purposes, generally financed by the local authorities themselves.

Places like Dusseldorf, Frankfurt, Hamburg and Potsdam were soon to witness the embryo airline operations of Delag. This municipal collaboration did much to succour the Zeppelin cause and provided flying hours and specialised experience to crewmen and design staff alike. Out of these operations came the priceless know-how which later enabled both the Army and the Navy to mobilise their own separate Zeppelin forces.

Delag immediately placed an order for an improved ship, LZ-7, but in a sense this could only magnify the overall deficit of the two companies. In the early part of 1910, the German Army took over LZ-5 as their second Zeppelin airship and accordingly labelled it Z-2. Based on the army aerodrome at Cologne, Z-2 made a further sixteen very successful flights under the command of Major Sperling, but due to a combination of very high winds and a lack of experience on the part of the military ground handling party was wrecked on 24th April.

On 19th June the new Delag LZ-7, incorporating the technical advances required by the world's first airline, was launched. This splendid ship, known to Dr Durr as "type E", could not be permitted to fly under the uninspiring identity of a works serial number; it was christened *Deutschland*.

The *Deutschland* was immediately posted to Dusseldorf under the command of a new captain by the name of Kahlenberg. Nine days and seven flights later she lay wrecked in the Teutoburger forest, forced down by engine failure. The LZ-6 immmediately went into regular service for another thirty-four flights, during which she transported a total of 726 passengers safely. Her service ended in an accidental fire in the hangar where she was temporarily housed at Baden-Oos in September, bringing the operations of 1910 to a miserable end.

Only the primitive LZ-3 now remained intact in Germany and that was in the possession of the Army. Not until March, 1911, would another Zeppelin take to the air. In ten years, seven experimental ships had been built and six of them accidentally destroyed, but no lives had been lost.

While the airship was being projected as the fashionable new mode of travel, none but the most simple-minded saw the Zeppelin as being anything but the deadly new weapon of war that the Press of the world claimed it to be. Rather more to the point was the succession of secret reports prepared by the British watchdog, the Committee of Imperial Defence, and its satellite sub-committees. Late in 1908 it was recorded that:

> ". . . the full potentialities of airships and the dangers to which we might be exposed by their use, can only be ascertained definitely by building them ourselves. This was the original reason for constructing submarines and in their case the policy has been completely vindicated. The Committee are of opinion that the rigid type of airship should be adopted in the case of naval experiments . . . a sum of £35,000 should be allotted to the Admiralty for the purpose of building a dirigible balloon. There appears to be no necessity for the Government to continue experiments in aeroplanes, provided that advantage is taken of private enterprise in this form of aviation."

Britain's first "Zeppelin," H.M.A. No. 1, afloat in the assembly hangar at the Vickers yard at Barrow-in-Furness in May, 1911.   *Eric Morgan*

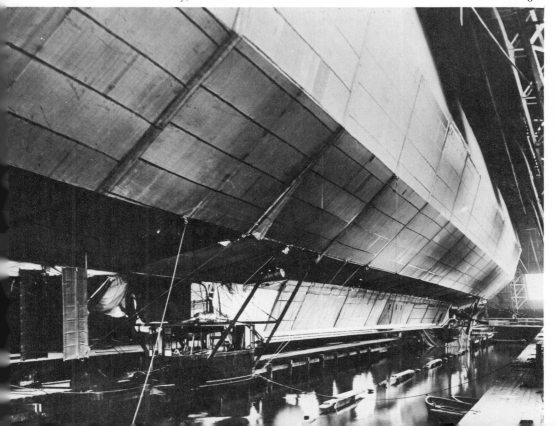

The eight-cylinder Wolseley engine of H.M.A. No. 1 which developed 180 b.h.p.

R.A.E.Cardington, Crown copyright

This, of course, was the prelude to the contract that was awarded to Vickers on 7th May, 1909, so one can fairly accept that by 1910 Britain had committed herself to a similar path of air-weapon development to that taken by Germany. The very big difference between the two "Establishments" was in the matter of the hard-earned experience already available to the German Government but lacking in Britain.

Among those principally responsible for determining how the new airship was to be built were Captain R. H. S. Bacon on the Admiralty side and Mr C. Robertson, Chief Engineer at Vickers at Barrow, and Mr Hunt on the Vickers side.

Out of their deliberations came the design of H.M.A. No. 1, dubbed by the press *Mayfly*, with the following general specification:

Overall length	512 feet
Diameter	48 feet
Displacement (or maximum volume)	663, 518 cubic feet (R.A.E. Records)
Engines	2 × 180 h.p. each
Gondolas	2
Propellers	4 (2 to each engine)
Gas cells	17
Gross weight	20.7 tons
Anticipated Useful Lift	No record found
Anticipated Maximum Speed	42 m.p.h.

Mayfly was 66 feet longer than her German contemporary, LZ-6, and 50 per cent greater in volume. Not only should this have given her a correspondingly greater lift value than LZ-6 but, because *Mayfly* was constructed with duralumin instead of aluminium four years earlier than the Zeppelins, further assets should have accrued. Her beautiful watertight mahogany engine-cars had been craftsman built by Saunders on the Isle of Wight, each one carrying a water-cooled, straight-eight Wolseley engine developed from a well-tried marine racing engine. Each engine drove a pair of 15-foot diameter wooden propellers at half engine speed, the propellers being mounted well outboard of the gondolas.

It was difficult for anyone to have evolved an efficient rigid airship in those days without emulating what had come to be standard Zeppelin practices, and *Mayfly* was proof of this. This even extended to the idea of trimming the centre of gravity by winching a weight along the length of the ship's keel, as had been tried in the original LZ-1 and afterwards abandoned.

Fortunately, the designers of *Mayfly* did not expect it to perform entirely without elevators and rudders, items which were being provided by the Short Brothers' new company. A great deal of enthusiastic ingenuity became manifest in attempts, principally by Admiralty people, to load the *Mayfly* with a lot of bright ideas that would never have been found on a genuine Zeppelin; apart from things like an anchor and a capstan, the one really intelligent piece of equipment was a condenser system for the recovery of water from the engine exhaust gases, a feature intended to compensate for the loss of trim following the consumption of fuel during flight.

Although its sheer deadweight made it impractical and the condenser apparatus had to be removed, the basic idea was effectively resurrected in the much bigger ships of the 1930s. As *Mayfly* began to approach completion and inflation was carried out, it was evident that her final weight had been seriously underestimated and she would not be able to fly. When she was eventually taken out into the waters of the Cavendish Dock in May, 1911, her builders were devastated to find that despite having dumped a considerable number of fittings and loose equipment, at least another three tons needed to be removed before there could be any hope of the ship becoming airborne.

Captain Bacon was originally appointed as the senior overseer, assisted by Captain Murray Sueter and Commander Oliver Schwann. When Captain Bacon reached retirement age in 1909 he was succeeded by Murray Sueter with the new status of Inspecting Captain of Airships, a post to which he devoted his enormous energy and enthusiasm to the exclusion of all else. Schwann, already a talented pilot with inventive qualities, found little to keep him occupied and as a result applied himself during his residence at Barrow to the development of the first successful British seaplane on floats. He later went on to achieve a great deal more in the field of military flying and eventually retired from the R.A.F. as an Air Vice-Marshal.

An important recruit to the Barrow scene in April, 1911, was Commander E. A. Masterman, who was devoted to the airship cause and pursued it intensively throughout the First World War.

Between May and September, 1911, drastic surgery was performed on *Mayfly*,

19

involving the removal of the main keel, the modification and interchanging of the two engine-cars, and alterations to the propeller transmission systems.

On 24th Septmber nothing remained but to put the results to the test, and it is at this critical point that a strange fog descended on what actually happened when *Mayfly* was brought out of her waterside hangar for testing. The most commonly accepted version of the event is that a sudden beam wind smote the partially exposed hull of the ship just as she was emerging from the hangar, and that the resulting distortions broke her completely in two. Since this was precisely the sort of thing that had been troubling the Zeppelins in Germany, it is not an unreasonable assumption. The fact is, however, that most accounts of the affair are notable for their speculations rather than their confirmations.

The inquiry that was held over the remains of *Mayfly* was attended by the celebrated Rear Admiral Sturdee, to whom was attributed the now legendary remark when he first beheld the wreckage "The work of an idiot!" What does appear to be the truth about *Mayfly's* demise has come to light, revealing how very apt was Sturdee's famous remark.

In the autumn of 1973 when the author was discussing this problem with Air Marshal Sir Victor Goddard, our last surviving rigid airship captain, the facts were revealed in all their horrific simplicity. Although Sir Victor was seventy-seven at the time of our conversations, his mind was crystal clear concerning a matter related to him by Sir Barnes Wallis. It transpired that Sir Barnes during the time of his own preoccupation with airships at Vickers at Barrow had been on very good terms with Commander E. A. Masterman, and the two had commonly shared confidences on topics concerning airships as a matter of mutual interest.

According to Masterman, *Mayfly* was pulled in half by the handling party when someone forgot to release the lines that tethered the bows of the ship.

What was happening in the Zeppelin camp at a time when Barrow had thought they were about to catch up with Friedrichshafen? A replacement *Deutschland*, LZ-8, of identical design was brought out from Friedrichshafen on the last day of March, 1911. With Dr Eckener in charge of the new *Deutschland* at a prestige operational base at Dusseldorf, all seemed set fair for a very successful summer for Delag.

By 16th May, LZ-8 had already clocked up forty-seven flying hours in twenty-two flights. As passengers began filing aboard for the twenty-third flight, the unfortunate Dr Eckener was about to receive the toughest lesson he ever had cause to learn. Already apprehensive about the prevailing weather conditions, he allowed his judgement to be overruled by an anxiety not to disappoint his customers and permitted the vessel to be brought out of its hangar with its precious cargo of passengers already aboard.

When one examines photographs showing how the LZ-8 was impaled on the hangar roof by the force of the wind, one can only guess at the torture inflicted on the ever-cautious Hugo Eckener. Never again would he allow anybody or any

"The work of an idiot!" H.M.A. No. 1 wrecked while being taken from its hangar on 24th September, 1911.   *W. Ballantyne*

circumstances to sway his judgement as to whether a ship was ready to fly. The accident contributed to his later becoming one of the foremost meteorological specialists in Germany.

During the time *Mayfly* was in the news in 1911, two further Zeppelins were delivered, LZ-9 and LZ-10. Both were of the newest "type F", the first to be built with the big new Maybach engines of 145 h.p. which boosted maximum speeds to over 47 m.p.h. With a gas volume of 628,000 cubic feet in seventeen gas cells, the value for Useful Lift was now some 14,300 pounds, an advance of more than 3,000 pounds over the previous "type E" *Deutschland*. LZ-10 was launched on 26th June, a little over three months earlier than the LZ-9 on 2nd October, the former ship being urgently needed by Delag while the latter went to the German Army as EZ-2, the "E" being the abbreviation for "ersatz" since it was the replacement for the wrecked Z-2.

The Schutte-Lanz company, of Mannheim, had gone into the same profession and 1911 also saw appearance of the first of their intriguing new designs. If only because the history of Schutte-Lanz became inadvertently entwined with that of Cardington, notice must be taken of its achievements in the world of the rigid airship. Inhibited partly by Zeppelin patents, or so it was suggested to the author by

The Schutte-Lanz factory at Mannheim as it was in 1973, more than half a century after its airship-building exploits.   *Herr Schneider*

the late Hans von Schiller, Johannes Schutte not only adopted a near-perfect streamline profile for his first ship but also ignored the well-established Zeppelin construction system using prefabricated aluminium girders. From the very beginning he went in for timber construction, and by applying his extensive knowledge of the physical sciences he evolved an extensive range of girder modules, contrived from thin plywood sheets glued together with cold-water casein cement and reinforced with hardwood blocks and mild steel sheet fittings at the appropriate stress points. The resulting structure of the first Schutte-Lanz airship SL-1 produced a hull that was a well-streamlined teardrop shape, fashioned from full-length girders laid end to end of the hull, not in the parallel style of the Zeppelin but in two opposing spirals, like the overlapping wickerwork of an ordinary wastepaper basket; possibly the nearest modern counterpart has been the "geodetic" fuselage of the Wellington bomber.

The structure of SL-1 was a fascinating example of clever design in combination with skilled craftsmanship. Its diameter at the widest point was 60 feet and its overall length of 432 feet made it comparable in volume at three quarters of a million cubic feet with the orthodox Zeppelins of that period. Like all rigid airships, it contained its lifting hydrogen in multiple cells, eleven of them as against the typical fifteen to eighteen of the Zeppelins. Unlike the Zeppelins, however, special care was taken to ensure that hydrogen vented from the automatic pressure valves was fed to atmosphere by ducts in order to prevent the accumulation of an explosive gas-air mixture within the confines of the envelope. Not until 1916 did Friedrichshafen adopt this elementary precaution, despite having paid a terrible price for this omission with the naval L-2 in 1913.

Three weeks after *Mayfly* had been pulled in half, SL-1 graced the skies above Mannheim on 17th October.

During the seven or so years that Schutte-Lanz was building ships for both the Army and Navy, output was never prolific. Although it could hardly be claimed that the Schutte-Lanz company posed a threat to the Zeppelin company, its existence was encouraged by the German ministries possibly for much the same reason that in Britain the Admiralty was concerned to see that Vickers should not create its own monopoly. One of the more curious aspects of the German official attitude towards their two big airship companies was the veto placed on foreign sales. Colsmann and Eckener were desperate for orders from 1910 to 1912 and it was only by declaring a willingness to sell to Britain that contracts were given somewhat grudgingly. The German establishment had still to be convinced that Zeppelins in effective quantities were going to be needed.

CHAPTER THREE

The Rigid Airship goes to War

AFTER the fiasco of *Mayfly*, two years elapsed before the imminence of war persuaded the Admiralty to commission Vickers to build a replacement. Development work recommenced in 1913 under the direction of H. B. Pratt, originally a Barrow employee but latterly on the design staff of J. S. White, boatbuilders at Cowes on the Isle of Wight. Vickers quickly retrieved him and installed him in their London office in Victoria Street, soon to be joined there by the young Barnes Neville Wallis, his recent colleague and companion at White's.

Together, they and a few others settled down to designing the new rigid, to be known as H.M.A. No. 9, but when war broke out on 4th August, 1914, Wallis immediately volunteered for service with the Royal Navy. In less than twenty-four hours Vickers had contrived his return to the drawing board, but more than two years would pass before the fruits of this effort would show.

The two separate Zeppelin forces of Germany were caught flatfooted on the outbreak of war, with the Navy being in the worse position with only one Zeppelin. Already in the autumn of 1913 the L-1 had been destroyed in a thunderstorm over the North Sea, involving the death of the first "Leader of Airships", Korvettan-kapitän (Commander) Paul Metzing. Only a month later, a new and highly experimental L-2 exploded in mid-air near Berlin with the loss of all hands. This left the Naval Zeppelin Division with no Zeppelins whatever until May, 1914, barely three months before the outbreak of war. Shortly before this, a naval gunnery officer had been detached from the Grand Fleet for a posting to the Zeppelin service as a replacement for Paul Metzing. His name was Peter Strasser.

Only L-3 existed on 4th August and all Strasser could do for some months was to give his crews handling experience, cruising the coastlines watching for a possible British invasion. Surprisingly, no attempts were made to attack the supply ships and troopships pouring across the English Channel to reinforce the French Army.

The German Army did have ten large rigids available to them, but three of these were civil ships, used principally for training and also shared with naval crews. One of the Delag ships, LZ-17 *(Sachsen)*, did go into operational service for a while under the command of Ernst Lehmann. Generally speaking, most of the Army ships had been deployed to the eastern and the western fronts, but several were unserviceable and in some cases not even inflated. Certainly, despite all the alarms and fears in the west, nothing even resembling an all-out "War in the Air" could possibly have been envisaged at that time.

Because it was expected that opposition in the east would be less intense, ships allocated to that region were not only fewer in number but also of lower quality in respect to their age and design. The activities of these early Zeppelins on the eastern front did not last long, but despite errors of inexperience, the ships and their crews gave better service than might have been expected. Z-4, for example, undertook a number of long-distance reconnaissance flights, mainly in daylight, and flew scouting operations at the Battle of Tannenberg, these efforts being considered "significant". It was, however, a time when the general staff were far from certain how best the new

Korvettenkapitän (later Fregattenkapitän) Peter Strasser, who took over command of the German naval Zeppelins and did a great deal to upgrade the quality of Zeppelin technology. *Kurt Puzicha*

weapon should be employed. By the end of August, 1914, the Army had lost four of its big rigids to enemy action, and most of its others had been damaged. In each of the four losses, the ship was forced down by gunfire damage releasing great quantities of hydrogen without fire or explosion taking place or total crew loss.

When raids on Antwerp were carried out many international newspapers which had already created a stir over Germany's invasion of Belgium went into full cry over the atrocity of these bombings, which were among the earliest ever directed against great cities. Lehmann admits being responsible for the first of these, performed with the old *Sachsen*, but points out the fact that in the course of the Belgian retreat, Antwerp was a fortified city blocking the German advance.

The Germans were not alone in planning air attacks on important targets. It is on record that as early as 13th August the British Admiralty were proposing to bomb the naval dockyards at Kiel and Wilhelmshaven, though the raids were not carried out because of the lack of suitable aircraft. As Sir Walter Raleigh remarked in the official history *The War in the Air*, the Royal Naval Air Service from the first sought every opportunity for offensive action.

Among the pilots who flew across to Ostend on 27th August were two whose names would very soon become household words for their daring attacks on German Zeppelin bases. One non-rigid airship, H.M.A. No. 17 *(Beta)*, also went across, three officers who were in charge of it, Commander N. F. Usborne, Lieutenant W. C. Hicks and Lieutenant E. H. Sparling, becoming prominent airshipmen in the later years of the British rigids.

On 1st September, 1914, Winston Churchill cabled the French Ministry of Marine to the effect that "The Admiralty considers it extremely important to deny the use of territory within a hundred miles of Dunkirk to German Zeppelins and to attack by aeroplanes all airships found replenishing there. With your permission, the Admiralty wish to take all necessary measures to maintain aerial command of this region . . . we hope it may be accorded a free initiative . . . the immunity of Portsmouth, Chatham and London from dangerous aerial attack is clearly involved."

This message became the mandate for Wing Commander C. R. Samson, in command of the first naval air unit to be sent abroad, to wage a personal war against the Germans in his region, whether by sea, land or in the air. The first raids on Zeppelin bases took place on 22nd September but proved abortive.

In the autumn of 1914 Antwerp began to crumble under the German offensive and refugees streamed out from the city. Behind Antwerp at Morbecque, Samson's force was already within range of enemy guns and there were plans to fall back on Dunkirk to hold the Channel ports. It was decided to make another strike at a Zeppelin base while they were still within range of their naval aircraft. On 8th October, with poor visibility, two Sopwiths set out for Dusseldorf and Cologne. Squadron Commander Spenser Gray was airborne for three and a half hours but failed to locate the Cologne sheds, so instead bombed the railway station before returning to base. Flight Lieutenant Marix in the other aeroplane was more fortunate and his bombs turned the Dusseldorf hangers containing Captain Horn's brand new Z-9 into a holocaust. For the time being, after the collapse of the Antwerp sector, other demands made on the R.N.A.S. locally precluded any further attacks on the Zeppelin bases.

A bombing strike into German territory was a matter for careful organisation. Engines were notoriously unreliable, navigation instruments were primitive and speeds pathetically low in anything of a headwind. Loaded with fuel and bombs, aircraft were unable to reach useful safe altitudes, while unheated open cockpits often left pilots with frostbitten extremities. The crews had to be physically tough and courageous as well as technically sound and aeronautically proficient.

The men selected at the end of October for an attack on the Zeppelin factories at

Friedrichshafen were all these. Masterminded by Lieutenant Pemberton Billing, the operation was controlled from a French airship station at Belfort in the south of France. The pilots chosen to make the attack were Squadron Commander E. F. Briggs, Flight Commander J. T. Babington, Flight Lieutenant S. V. Sippe and Flight Sub-Lieutenant R. P. Cannon. The aircraft provided were Avro 504Ks, powered by 80 h.p. le Rhone rotary engines. All four aeroplanes and twelve mechanics arrived at Belfort in the middle of November. The pilots had been thoroughly briefed on the hazards of the four-hour flight and each machine carried four 20 lb Hales bombs. On the morning of 21st November, Squadron Commander Briggs was the first to get away, followed at five-minute intervals by his three companions. Cannon, the last to taxi out, had to give up with a damaged undercarriage.

Fully laden, the underpowered Avro of 1914 had to be flown solo and the pilots were at great risk in their unarmed aeroplanes. Reaching the target zone undetected, the machines first climbed to about a thousand feet before diving to attack the Zeppelin works to the north of the town.

Once alerted, the Germans put up a spirited defence with rifle fire, machine guns and small cannon. As the great hydrogen plant went skywards in one fantastic sheet of flame, a direct hit on the main assembly hall wreaked further destruction. Briggs' aircraft was brought down in flames and he had to be rescued by garrison troops as infuriated workers laid into him with fists and boots. The raid was a total success.

The 20 lb. Hales bomb was a widely used weapon by British aircraft in the early stages of the First World War.   *Author*

Not until late in the Second World War, when it was discovered that V2s were being assembled there, was Friedrichshafen again attacked.

Despite the spectacular damage done during that first raid, production and deliveries to the two services scarcely faltered. At that time the naval L-3 was in service; this was the first of the "M type" ships, a design temporarily frozen in order to get ships into quantity production quickly, even though the type was seen to be already obsolete.

Uncomfortably aware of this unpalatable fact, Strasser fought hard to secure the new ships coming off the assembly lines, having to contend with strong opposition from the Army Command. For the rest of the year, Strasser was less concerned to involve his service in hostile activities than to build up his fleet of airships and train his crews to reasonable levels of efficiency. His first addition, just a fortnight after the outbreak of war, was LZ-27, which became L-4 and the command of which was given to Count von Platen. Sister-ship LZ-28 came along exactly a month later and was given to Klaus Hirsch as L-5.

With the Army getting their share of new airships, it was 3rd November before Strasser obtained another ship, LZ-31, which became L-6. Though their deeds were seldom spectacular, the crew that took over L-6 were to remain substantially the same throughout the rest of the war and would be engaged in most of the major

Under the command of Oberleutnant-zur-See Horst Freiherr von Buttlar-Brandenfels, centre left, and Hans von Schiller, centre right, this crew became an elite Zeppelin crew, being given the newest types of ship and some of the more important missions. The seaman ringed is Pruss, in later years to become commander of the *Hindenburg*.   *Kurt Puzicha*

operations carried out by the naval Zeppelins during that time. Their commander, Oberleutnant-zur-See Horst Freiherr von Buttlar-Brandenfels, more widely known as von Buttlar, was to be the only member of the Force other than Strasser to be awarded the Pour le Mérite, colloquially known as "The Blue Max". His First Officer was Hans von Schiller who, with Hugo Eckener and Ernst Lehmann, went on to command the passenger Zeppelins between the two World Wars. When von Schiller, last of the great Zeppelin commanders, died on 7th December, 1976, the author lost a good friend who had contributed a great deal to the authenticity of this book. By coincidence, another good friend, Captain George Meager, First Officer of the last British rigid, R.100, died that same day.

The L-7 and L-8 were the last two Zeppelins to be commissioned into the Navy in 1914; L-7 was commanded by Werner Peterson, later killed in L-32 at Billericay, and L-8 by Helmut Beelitz. At the end of 1914 the Army had lost five rigids and only two new ships had been added, Z-10 (Hauptmann Horn) and Z-11 (Hauptman Gaissert), the first of many from factories other than Friedrichshafen.

At the end of the year, the Frankfurt plant was almost ready to hand over to the Army a much-improved Zeppelin, the LZ-26, to go into service with Lehmann as Z-12 at the beginning of 1915. This was the "type N". Significant improvements were the enclosure of the gondolas for the first time, an increase in speed of 4 m.p.h. and in lift of three tons.

By the end of 1914, the Naval Zeppelin Force had reached parity with the Army and had six serviceable Zeppelins. The five months had been devoted almost exclusively to training flights, and their year ended without the loss of a single rigid.

Crew training went smartly ahead, as did also the consolidation of the all-important maintenance ground staff. Most valuable of all was the progress made with new and strategically sited hangars and hydrogen plants, foremost among them the new station at Nordholz, just behind Cuxhaven, near the mouth of the River Elbe. Beginning with the remarkable revolving double hangar of 1914, the station became steadily enlarged during the ensuing years until it boasted six hangars in all, two "singles" and four "doubles". By August, 1918, a total of ten rigids could be accommodated, supplied and serviced at this station, the H.Q. of the Naval Zeppelin Force for almost the whole of the war.

With Zeppelins that were low in performance and already obsolete in design, and with volunteer aircrews having only a minimum of experience, operations over the North Sea and Baltic in the winter of 1914–15 were extremely hazardous. Clearly the Force was not yet in a position to take direct hostile action against Britain.

On Christmas Day the Royal Navy set out to give the Zeppelin Force a surprise, the attack being another in the series designed to scorch out the Zeppelins in their nests. In this instance, the target was the brand new installation at Nordholz and the aeroplanes to be used were seaplanes, to be launched over the side of the ships that carried them close to Heligoland and Germany. Early on Christmas Eve a little armada set sail for Heligoland; there were three aircraft-carrying ships, the modified cross-channel ferries *Engadine*, *Empress* and *Riviera*, escorted by the light cruisers *Arethusa* and *Undaunted* and eight destroyers. A further two destroyers and ten submarines already at sea were detailed to give additional co-operation and in particular to keep a sharp lookout for any seaplane unable to return to its parent ship.

Just after dawn on Christmas Day, seven of the seaplanes rose from the water and went off to bomb the Zeppelin sheds at Nordholz and reconnoitre for enemy ships in the harbours and docks of the region. Early wireless activity revealed that the element of surprise was already lost and the first scouting Zeppelin was seen as early as 07.35 hours. L-3 and L-4 were grounded by fog at Hamburg but L-5 and L-6 took off from Nordholz and managed to monitor almost every manoeuvre made, both by the attacking ships and by their seaplanes. One of the bombers found Nordholz but failed to score any hits. Baron von Buttlar in L-6 played a leading role in this action, the details of which were related to the author first-hand, sixty years afterwards, still astonishingly fresh in the mind of Buttlar's compatriot, von Schiller:

"On the morning of that day, we were ordered to take off immediately as a British formation had been sighted north-west of Heligoland. When we reached the specified area, we saw a formation appear from the west, approaching Heligoland some forty miles out from the coastline of Germany. In the lead we found two British cruisers, *Arethusa* and *Undaunted*, whilst coming on behind were several destroyers accompanied by three ships which we took for minelayers. Only after the war did we discover they were aircraft carriers. As the winds began to stiffen, we could only close up with the flotilla quite slowly, but soon the cruisers and destroyers began to open fire on us but their shots were not reaching us, the bursts falling short and passing beneath us. Eventually we got close up to the last ship and when we were nearly on top of it, ready to loose off our cargo of bombs, we saw the Englishmen aiming at us with their rifles and machine guns and could actually hear the bullets striking parts of our ship. We immediately replied with our own machine-guns, spraying the decks and causing the crew to scatter for cover. Unhappily all our bombs missed the target, the nearest one exploding some 30 metres astern of the ship, and in any case L-6 very soon had to withdraw as a result of the gas losses being caused by the hits we had received, but we still tried to keep the formation in sight. We did actually try to get a wireless message sent off to the Admiral of the Fleet but our rather primitive apparatus let us down at the critical time and we were unable to transmit. At this point, von Buttlar decided to turn back since we were losing height steadily, but we managed to overfly the Admiral's ship which we located at Schillig Reede near Wilhelmshaven and there we successfully dropped a message bag on to the cruiser's deck. We got back eventually to Nordholz, but by then the L-6 had lost so much buoyancy and had become so heavy that we had to jettison not only all our ballast but nearly all our remaining petrol in order to make something of a reasonable landing."

Towards the end of the action, Hirsch and Wenke in L-5 just missed catching three of the British seaplanes on the water near the waiting submarine E.11. To the accompaniment of a salvo of bombs, the last of the aircrews scrambled up into the conning tower and E.11 crash-dived, leaving the seaplanes to be riddled with machine-gun fire from the L-5.

CHAPTER FOUR

The Original Long-Range Bomber

SECRET

January 1st, 1915

Memorandum for the War Council

Information from a trustworthy source has been received that the Germans intend to make an attack on London by airships on a great scale at any early opportunity.

The Director of the Air Department reports that there are approximately twenty German airships which can reach London now from the Rhine, carrying each a ton of high explosive.

They could traverse the English part of the journey, coming and going, in the dark hours. The weather hazards are considerable, but there is no known means of preventing the airships coming, and not much chance of punishing them on their return. The unavenged destruction of non-combatant life, may therefore be very considerable.

Having given most careful consideration to this subject, and taken every measure in their power, the Air Department of the Admiralty must make it plain that they are quite powerless to prevent such an attack if it is launched with good fortune and in favourable weather conditions.

I attach a paper by the Director of the Air Department.

W.S.C.

This document, prepared by Winston Churchill, then First Lord of the Admiralty, must surely rate as the most historic confession of the technological age. After the ebullient optimism of the earlier months, this incredible admission of defeat before the battle had begun was proof, if any were needed, that the rigid airship had become a power to be reckoned with. So great was the impact of these few lines that a major meeting of the War Council was convened on 7th January, 1915, under the chairmanship of the Prime Minister, Herbert Asquith, those present including Lord Haldane, Lord Crewe, Mr Churchill, Mr Balfour, Admiral Lord Fisher, Admiral Sir A. K. Wilson, Mr Lloyd George, Lord Kitchener and General Sir J. Wolfe Murray.

Churchill reminded everyone that before the war the responsibility for Home Defence lay with the War Office, but when the war began they were so busy getting the B.E.F. over to France that the Admiralty had offered to undertake the aerial defence of London. He revealed that he had ten aeroplanes at Dunkirk as his first line of defence "whose primary functions were to prevent the completion of airship bases in Belgium and to attack any airships which might call in that country for supplies". Any Zeppelins that evaded this net would automatically encounter "some sixty aeroplanes always ready in the triangle enclosed between London, Sheerness and Dover . . . these aeroplanes were armed with rifles firing incendiary bullets . . . in addition he believed that some flyers were prepared to charge a Zeppelin. Within the

The naval crew of L-3, the first long-range bomber in history. The officers in the control car are, left to right, Paul Puzicha (navigator), Hans Fritz (commander), von Buttlar (first officer), and an unknown officer. *Kurt Puzicha*

same triangle there are a total of 76 anti-aircraft guns. In London itself there are two 3-inch, four 6-pounders, and six pom-poms with 13 searchlights".

Never before had the War Council dealt with so provocative a subject as the imminent defence needs of London, and the arguments concerning it raged for a considerable time, with some of the contributions displaying more panic than intelligence. One of the more prophetic items of information volunteered was that Lord Fisher had "reliable information that an attack would be made, first by the German Naval Zeppelins on some east coast town, and subsequently a combined attack by naval and military airships on London".

The prospect of being bombed had long been anticipated by the British press and by a fair proportion of the public, though little or nothing had been done to prepare for it because there was no precedent to go on.

In Germany, plans for bombing raids on Britain had been made during the previous autumn; yet oddly enough, the agitation was less from the Services than from the press and, as a result, from the German public.

Those two loveliest of counties, Norfolk and Suffolk, have over the years probably witnessed more airship activities of all kinds than any other two counties in England. It was apparent that the wartime Zeppelins favoured the East Anglian promontory for their first landfall before fanning out in search of particular targets. A glance at the map reveals how very conveniently positioned it was in relation to the Zeppelin bases in north Germany. The historic seaport of Great Yarmouth became the object of both the first and the last Zeppelin attacks on Britain; Strasser was in command of both raids, in which matters went utterly wrong for him.

In Germany bickering took place among the higher echelons of both Army and Navy Zeppelin Services as to whether future raids upon England should be made in collaboration or as separate exercises. Strasser became fractious with the overall situation, being aware that his ships were not up to the level of performance needed; only the brief period of very low air temperatures could help to compensate for this handicap, since this increased the quality of lift. The alternative was to delay such activities until bigger and better Zeppelins came into service. Significantly, Fisher had forecast to the War Council that when the Zeppelins came, they would be almost certain to come over at night and when the air temperature was close to freezing.

By 7th January Strasser was given the all clear, except for the proviso that the Kaiser was still forbidding any attacks on the City of London. A first attempt on 13th January was aborted due to bad weather, but as the forecasts improved in the following days, preparations were again organised at Fuhlsbuttel and Nordholz, and L-3, L-4 and L-6, the flagship, were made ready. Strasser detailed L-3 and L-4 to attack Norfolk while he in L-6, with Buttlar and Schiller, would test out the opposition with a thrust into the Thames estuary in the direction of London.

L-6 left Nordholz shortly after half past nine on the morning of 19th January, an hour ahead of L-3 and L-4 from Fuhlsbuttel. At an early stage, Strasser had to accept a major failure of one of the two Maybach engines in the rear car, and rather than risk further trouble L-6 returned to Nordholz, arriving in darkness at about half past six.

Staying within sight of each other as long as possible, L-3 and L-4 pressed on through slowly deteriorating weather. The two ships droned on and on over the open sea, crewmen peering out apprehensively as wind strength increased and driving sleet began weighing the ships down. In the engine-cars, which were open to the elements, there was mounting tension and stress.

Later generations of airship specialists have paid tribute to the excellence of navigation standards attained under such bad conditions; the real credit should go specifically to Paul Puzicha, the navigating officer of L-3. On the night of 19th January, 1915, police observers logged L-4 as having crossed the coast at five minutes to eight and L-3 at five minutes past. Some writers quote nine o'clock but this time, derived from Zeppelin logs, was Central European Time and not Greenwich Mean Time. From that moment, everything turned in favour of the bewildered attackers.

The chart logged from observers' reports of the raid shows that L-3 and L-4 split up as soon as they crossed the coast and went off in opposite directions, hugging the coastline. Initially they had both arrived at a point midway between Cromer and Yarmouth, and as L-4 made off north-west for the Wash and Hunstanton, circling Cromer on the way, L-3 made direct for Great Yarmouth, coming in over the North Denes at 8.25 p.m. From the glow in the sky, Fritz knew this was no small fishing village. As he headed due south, a mere two or three hundred yards inshore, he commenced to bomb the town from one end to the other in a fairly straight line.

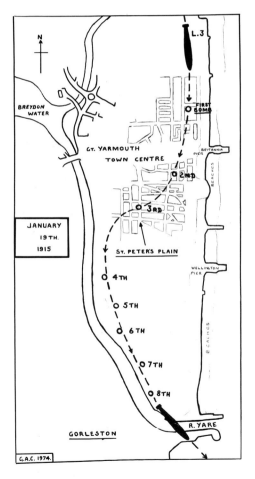

The flight-path of L-3 over Great Yarmouth on the night of 19th January, 1915, estimated by the author from reports of the raid.

Yarmouth that night was unquestionably what would now be reckoned to be a very soft target, while the whole of the southern tip of the spit occupied by the Royal Naval Air Service Station certainly warranted but never received attention from the L-3. The Yarmouth crews eventually operated a mixture of landplanes, seaplanes and flying boats in their constant patrols against enemy forces, and their successes against the Zeppelins were enough to cause Strasser great concern. But on the night of 19th January, 1915, the hangars contained only three flyable aircraft, none of them armed.

When Fritz started his bombing run, his luck was better than he knew. Unimpeded by anti-aircraft guns, searchlights or fighter 'planes, he had an illuminated target spread out befor him like a flare-path. On the ground, people even stood around in clusters, puzzled and baffled rather than frightened. The first bomb

Samuel Smith (53) and Martha Taylor (72), the first victims of an air raid on Britain.
Norfolk County Libraries

buried itself with a muffled thud in the lawn of Mr Norford Suffling's house in Norfolk Square, three feet away from a window at the side of the tradesmen's entrance. The first long-range high explosive bomb to strike Britain was a dud; as also was the second one which, moments later, fell on Millers Stables at the back of 78 Crown Road. The third bomb was not a dud; 53-year-old Samuel Smith was decapitated as he stood outside his cobbler's shop on St Peter's Plain when the pavement in front of No. 25 opened up in a pillar of flame and blast. The body of 72-year-old spinster Martha Taylor from nearby Drakes Buildings lay close to the body of Mr Smith, the two of them the first British citizens to have died in an air raid.

The bomb, the third of eight 110-pounders dropped on the town that night, shattered windows over a radius of 150 yards, including those of St Peter's Church. Edward Ellis, the owner of No. 25, entered his house and closed the front door just in time. Despite the whole front of the house being ripped out, he sustained only

Damage to 25 St Peter's Plain, Great Yarmouth, caused in the air raid of 19th January, 1915, and the same house as it was in 1970.   *Norfolk County Libraries and author*

grazes and a bruise to the head. The house still shows signs of where it was damaged. Dr Leonard Ley, of nearby Alexandra Road, was on the scene immediately and attended an injured soldier in the street. For many years he wore a tiepin made from the bomb fragment he had extracted from his military patient. The next target to receive a direct hit was another stable, this time near South Quay at W. K. Mays, the local butcher, but the bomb failed to explode. Landlord Smith's *First & Last* tavern in Southgates Road emptied itself of uninjured clientele after the fifth bomb had excavated a hole in the roadway in front of the pub. By this time the raider was nearly up to the R.N.A.S. station, but since he continued dropping his bombs closer to the harbour, one is forced to conclude that he really did not know it was there. His last three bombs slanted closer to what was then the fish wharf area, one near Joe Steel's *Fishwharf Restaurant*, one near the Red Cross hospital on South Denes and the last one right on the end of the quay and almost aboard the steam drifter *Piscatorial*, which was slightly damaged. L-3 continued on for a few miles, passing along the seafront of Gorleston before turning back to cruise slowly again along the coastline looking out for L-4, but finally turning east for Germany.

Historian Mr Emms, of Gorleston, recalled in a letter to the author that he was conducting an auction at his place of business in King Street when the bombs fell. He heard the explosion in St Peter's Plain not far away, but took it for the sound of a road accident, and it was only when a few curious people who had left the hall returned with news of the destruction 200 yards away that he realised there had been an air raid.

Two days later at the inquest, Coroner J. Tolver Waters was reported by the *Yarmouth Independent* as stating that:

"There was absolutely no doubt that the bombs were thrown from a hostile airship belonging to the enemy of this country and that it came here with the purpose of committing wanton destruction and the taking of life, which according to his mind and that of every reasonable thinking person was nothing short of murder, plain and simple! (hear-hear!). . . Of course under ordinary circumstances if anything happened to cause loss of life by anyone's hands, that person would rightly hang but in this case he could not get the right person. The person in question was carrying out the orders of the authority under the Kaiser, but it was none the less murder. It will not be possible, as it would be your wish, to return a verdict of murder."

The Coroner had put the stamp of approval on British public opinion, and though his published report was really no more than his personal opinion, statements of this nature do come to be regarded as being official. It mirrored the sentiments of the time.

To most neutrals, including America, the Zeppelin rigid airship acquired a social stigma associated with blackmail and the murder of civilians, both highly emotive issues in the propaganda war. Though the aeroplane soon became far more potent in its ability to reduce the population, it failed to match the Zeppelin as the root of all evil in the minds of the public.

Viewed from the German Admiralty's standpoint, the effort involved in mounting this three-ship exercise was disproportionate to the results obtained. The only definite reactions to come out of the event were the stiffening of the British defences and an increase in the British recruitment figures.

When one reads of The Zeppelin Campaign, one should recognise it as being less of a concerted attack programme than an extended period of operational experiments. If the phrase Zeppelin Campaign has any significance at all, it is that it offers a convenient label covering the period of some twenty months from the

Members of Great Yarmouth Archaeological Society with a commemorative plaque which was mounted on 25 St Peter's Plain in 1981 as a result of moves initiated by the author. *Yarmouth Mercury*

The "M-type" L-3 (LZ-24) which was the only Zeppelin in service with the German navy at the outbreak of war.   *Kurt Puzicha*

January raid on Yarmouth until September, 1916, when such raiding was almost completely abandoned due to excessive losses.

In any case, airship operations over the sea during winter were hazardous enough, as the crews of the Yarmouth raiders discovered less than a month later when returning from a patrol off the Norwegian coast. Both L-3 and L-4 experienced failures of two of the three engines in each ship, preventing a return to base against a rising headwind. At different times and at different places, both ships ultimately gained the relative safety of Danish beaches. L-3 landed with only slight damage and was set on fire by the crew, and L-4 crashed into the sea just as it was about to cross the surfline. As most of the crew scrambled overboard to wade ashore, the hopelessly damaged ship took to the air and, with the force of the gale behind her, disappeared into the night over the North Sea. Four of the crew who were still aboard were never seen again.

Despite the unsuitability of their "type M" Zeppelins, Strasser's crews were quickly gaining experience, and only five days after the Great Yarmouth raid L-5 was ordered to the scene of the Battle of the Dogger Bank. This action, short and fierce, involved several capital ships, the Germans losing the cruiser *Blücher* while the British battle cruiser *Lion* was badly damaged. The L-5 was used here, as on several later occasions, close up to the German ships as though to protect them: it did not reconnoitre the British forces and so was unable to keep the German Admirals fully informed.

By the spring of 1915 the Naval Force was operating out of nine different airship stations covering the regions from Belgium through to Schleswig-Holstein and further east along the Baltic coast. About two dozen complete and fully trained aircrews were now available, and some four thousand ground staff were working in the various support services needed to keep the ships operational.

The Navy began the year with six Zeppelins, L-3 to L-8 inclusive, to which were added twelve more, L-9 to L-20 inclusive, in the course of the year. The original six were all of the old "type M" class; the new ships were all significantly improved ships, ten being of the new "P type", the first of which was delivered to the Army as LZ-38 in early April. LZ-40 was delivered to the Navy as L-10, which gave rise to the use of the rather imprecise term "the L-10 Class".

It may help in analysing the path of technical progress at later stages to take a look at the statistics of the L-3, with which the Navy first went to war:

General information relating to "type M" Zeppelins as represented by L-3	
Overall Length	518 feet
Diameter	48½ feet
Height	60 feet
Volumetric Capacity	794,000 cubic feet
Number of gas-cells	18
Power-cars	2 (Both open topped)
Engines	3 (Maybach type CX 200 h.p.)**
Propellers	4*
Gross Weight	57,000 pounds (Equal to maximum lift)
Useful Lift	20,000 pounds (Gross weight minus empty weight)
Maximum Speed	47 m.p.h.
Maximum Altitude	8,000 feet in optimum conditions
Typical range/duration	20-30 hours (800 miles?)
Fuel Consumption	One gallon per mile (very approximately)
Typical bomb load	800-1,000 pounds
Crew Complement	16
Ordered	21st March, 1914
Delivered	11th May, 1914
Crashed	17th Feb, 1915
Total of flights	138
Reconnaissance flights	27
Bombing raids	1

*Two driven from single engine in front power-car and two driven from two engines in rear power-car. All propellers were three-bladed and driven by outboard shafting.
**Engines were straight-six water-cooled side valve. An authentic specimen may be seen in London's Science Museum.

Twelve of the "M type" were built, from LZ-24 to LZ-37, but not including LZ-26 and LZ-36, which with LZ-25 may be seen as flying test-beds for an overall improvement programme; LZ-26 being a genuine prototype incorporating fundamental changes; LZ-25 embodying just one of LZ-26's more prominent changes; and LZ-36 embodying all LZ-26's improvements, together with a few more besides.

LZ-26, which as Z-12 became Lehmann's replacement for *Sachsen*, was unusual first for having been built at Frankfurt and second because it was originally designed just before the war as a more efficient civilian transport. Launched on 14th December, 1914, she incorporated improvements which were a good blend of past operational experience and a slightly larger volume, limited by the dimensions of the then available assembly halls. The extra ten feet in length imparted another 86,000 cubic feet in volume which, together with minor structural improvements, increased the Useful Lift by nearly 7,000 pounds. The more prominent outward changes were

Heinrich Mathy, most famous of all Zeppelin commanders. *Kurt Puzicha*

the enclosure of both power-cars for the first time and the replacement of the old-style multiple tail surfaces by the cleaner and more straightforward cruciform assembly already in vogue on Schutte-Lanz designs and tried out first on LZ-25 five months before. The overall cleaning up of the excrescences in this way added about 4 m.p.h. to the maximum speed and possibly improved fuel consumption slightly.

LZ-36 and LZ-39 were the first ships on the production line to embody the innovations of the famous Z-12, but they were regarded only as interim efforts pending the introduction of the big new "P type". LZ-39 went to the Army and retained its works number as its service number. LZ-36 went to the Navy and became the L-9, commanded by Heinrich Mathy, destined to become the most daring and successful of all Zeppelin commanders.

The new "P type" in the form of LZ-38 first appeared on 3rd April, 1915, and twenty-two such ships were constructed between then and 2nd February, 1916. The type constituted the first really practical Zeppelin weapon, incorporating as it did all the technical improvements to date together with an advance in physical size to more than one million cubic feet for the first time. An extra engine was fitted and the combined improvements in performance gave a maximum speed of 57 m.p.h. and a Useful Lift of 33,000 pounds as against the 20,000 pounds of the "M type". Instead of converting the forward car to take the additional engine and propeller in the same layout as in the rear car, the rear car itself accepted this engine with its "pusher" propeller, and thus was created the very successful standard three-engined rear gondola which endured nearly to the end of the war. The arrival of the "P type" ships was the first dramatic proof of the airship designer's code of practice which offers aerostatic efficiency only with great physical size.

The philosophy is simple but fundamental; once a weight estimate has been made for engines and crew and fuel, it becomes a simple matter to determine how much gas is needed to uplift it and, simultaneously, the weight of the gas-containing structure. All this time, the Zeppelins had been built just big enough to carry their own weight, but the moment the capacity exceeded a million cubic feet the benefits started coming in. The really important thing was that the increases in volume did not produce the same increases in length and diameter. The "R type" "Super-Zeppelins" of two million cubic feet had an overall length of about 650 feet, only about 110 feet longer than earlier ships of half the volume.

With better technical and productive support and building on hard-won operational experience, both services were able to consolidate their internal organisation and to start planning ahead for the first time.

The evidence of 1915's overall activities is usefully depicted by the summary analysis recorded in the following table:

Factors	Navy	Army	Total
Ships delivered from all factories	15	16	31
Zeppelins	12	14	26
Schutte-Lanz	3	2	5
Ships lost to enemy action	3	6	9
Ships lost in flying accidents	4	1	5
Ships lost in ground mishaps	2	2	4
Total lost from all causes	9	9	18
Ships in service at end of 1915	12	12	24

Notes

The twelve ships produced by Friedrichshafen was the highest annual total produced there. Löwenthal, the satellite to Friedrichshafen, produced seven and Potsdam near Berlin seven. All five of the Schutte-Lanz ships of 1915 were bigger than the Zeppelin "P type" and of slightly higher performance.

CHAPTER FIVE

The First Battle of Britain?

THE invasion of British air space begun on 19th January, 1915, continued unchecked through to the night of 2nd/3rd September, 1916. It was not until much later that the bombing aeroplanes of Germany took over the offensive from the defeated Zeppelins, but when it came the new form of attack was met with a great deal more resistance.

Combined counter-attacks by British fighter aircraft and the newly developed anti-aircraft batteries gave a new dimension to the air war over Southern Britain. Historian Raymond Fredette was so inspired by the drama played out over the Home Counties in the latter part of the First World War that he wrote an account under the title of *The First Battle of Britain*. Comparisons between the air wars of 1917/18 and of 1940 are certainly justified, and the fact that Britain owed its ability to cope in 1940 to the experience inherited from the First World War must not be overlooked. It was the slow but steady organisation of Home Defence throughout 1915/16 that eventually overcame the airship menace.

In twenty months of attacks, there were thirty-six Zeppelin raids with 146 separate flights by individual airships. Not all of the flights succeeded in crossing our coastline, the actual figure of 108 clearly revealing the hazardous nature of the flights on which they embarked. The most consistent feature of the so-called Zeppelin campaign was the occurrence of raids during the darkest of night-time conditions. Night flying posed no problems for the Zeppelin crews that were not infinitely more difficult and dangerous for the pilots of intercepting aeroplanes.

It was not long before a deadly competitiveness emerged between hunter and hunted; the struggle to gain and maintain the advantage of altitude became a technological race between the airships and the aeroplane; the physical endurance of fighter pilots was pitted against that of the airshipmen, both of them threatened by sub-zero temperatures and a rarified atmosphere; eventually the fate of the airships themselves became simply a question of the effectiveness of the missiles aimed at the giant hydrogen-filled vessels.

The only weapon that consistently succeeded was the machine-gun; and then only when the right grade of ammunition had been brought into use. Some varieties of ammunition were too dangerous to use in an aeroplane, due to their habit of exploding prematurely.

In the mutual contests for maximum altitudes, some Zeppelin commanders chose not to accept the weight penalties of their own defensive armaments, but they were few. Typically, a Zeppelin would be armed with six or even eight machine-guns of the 8mm Maxim-Nordenfeldt type with belt-feed ammunition. Some were mounted at the windows of the engine-gondolas, while one and sometimes two were mounted on tripods on the fully exposed observation platform on the top of the hull at the forward end. Another was usually provided on a mounting in a cockpit slotted into the hull just behind the great rudders.

Attacking British pilots eventually discovered that when they had secured a good firing position the opposition gunners stopped shooting, and it was believed that their guns were extremely unreliable. Several theories were advanced, until prisoners under interrogation disclosed that the stoppages were almost always due to the risk of igniting escaping hydrogen. When a ship is climbing rapidly, the expanding gas pours out from many points along the top of the envelope and could catch alight from the muzzle flashes of the ship's machine-guns.

Strasser saw that the historic first Yarmouth raid in January had only marginal merit, and it was a further three months before he attempted another exploratory sortie. The new and improved L-9 commanded by Mathy raided Tyneside on 14th April, 1915. The fact that a single ship could apparently attack the industrial north encouraged Strasser to try a relatively short-range attack on East Anglia with the three older ships L-5, L-6 and L-7. No sooner had Mathy reported his success on Tyneside, than Böcker, Buttlar and Peterson flew out in formation and inflicted heavy damage on Lowestoft, Maldon and other places. These were the activities on the part of the German Navy that served to agitate the rivalry of the Army people, in particular Erich Linnarz, who was within a fortnight testing the strength of the Thames Estuary defences. Flying the LZ-38, he left a string of bomb craters between

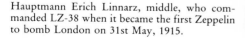
Hauptmann Erich Linnarz, middle, who commanded LZ-38 when it became the first Zeppelin to bomb London on 31st May, 1915.

Ipswich and Bury St Edmunds, and made no secret of the fact that he intended to penetrate the London defences before any of the Naval ships. As good as his word, throughout May, 1915, he made probing flights every week until on the very last night of the month he made good his boast as he bombed the East End of London right through Stoke Newington and Dalston to Whitechapel and Stepney.

From the defence standpoint it was an obvious German victory, showing the near impossibility of protecting Greater London with ground artillery. Linnarz was well aware of this and claimed to have deliberately baited the A.A. batteries near Southend, cruising around just out of range as they continued to fire innumerable shells in his general direction. Nine aeroplanes had been up that night but only one pilot got a brief sighting of LZ-38 and none came within shooting distance; two of the aeroplanes crashed and one pilot was killed.

The Navy resumed its raiding function as a direct result and on 4th June, 1915,

The Army airship LZ-38, the first Zeppelin to bomb London.
Kurt Puzicha

L-10 and SL-3, both from Nordholz, set out to raid Britain. The results were not conclusive, poor navigation being held to blame. Only two days afterwards both the Navy and Army set off to raid Britain independently. As it was mid-summer, the shorter nights limited the time it was possible to stay over Britain with reasonable safety; even periods of moonlight were avoided, the "safe" times being known to Zeppelin crews as *Fahrperioden*. Since reliable weather conditions were needed for the duration of a typical twenty-hour flight, good forecasting was vital. On this particular occasion, meterologists failed to predict the persistent fog that covered southern England and parts of the Channel. This was of no concern to Mathy, who again took the L-9 up north to inflict heavy damage in the docks region of Hull.

The Army sent out three ships, LZ-37, LZ-38, and LZ-39, to bomb London from the new Army bases in Belgium. Unfortunately for the Germans, matters began

Among the R.N.A.S. pilots responsible for driving the German army Zeppelins out of their Belgian bases were, left to right, Flight Lieutenant J. S. Mills, Flight Commander A. W. Bigsworth, Flight Lieutenant J. P. Wilson and Flight Sub-Lieutenant R. A. J. Warneford.

going wrong early. Some hours after the Zeppelins had started out, four British naval pilots took off from Dunkirk with the intention of attacking those same airships in their Belgian sheds. While Flight Lieutenant J. P. Wilson and Flight Lieutenant J. S. Mills in Henri Farman biplanes were heading for for Evere, Linnarz was already flying back there with engine trouble in his LZ-38; Flight Sub-Lieutenant R. A. J. Warneford in a high-wing, wire-braced Morane was on the way to Berchem St Agathe, his companion officer already having had to land with mechanical trouble.

Linnarz was the first back to base and saw his LZ-38 safely stowed away for the night. Otto van der Haegen in LZ-37 and Hans Masius in LZ-39 very soon had to turn back because of the fog. While Warneford was still on his way to the target area he saw LZ-37 on a converging course and rapidly began closing in for an attack. Instantly the ship's gunners began spraying him with bullets and a desperate race for height began. How this simple and not very efficient little aeroplane, handled with skill and determination, eventually outstripped the Zeppelin at 11,000 feet has become a classic of air combat history. Once above his target, Warneford flew the 200 yards along the top of the airship, releasing his four Hales bombs as he went; the results were instantaneous and spectacular. The ship almost disintegrated and Warneford's small aircraft flipped over on to its back with the eruption below. Quite amazingly, one crewman escaped the inferno as he plunged through the roof of a convent and bounced off a nun's bed; he lived to tell the tale for many years afterwards.

Almost at the same time, the pilots of the two Farmans were attacking the shed at Evere, now containing the returned LZ-38. Diving low into the darkness, they were met with strong opposition and had difficulty identifying their target; both pilots withdrew for a period while the early summer dawn spread sufficient light for

45

them to renew their attacks with more certainty. Dropping all their bombs through the thin-skinned roof of the hangar, they had the satisfaction of observing LZ-38's fiery and spectacular destruction.

After the earlier successes of Düsseldorf and Friedrichshafen, a single night's work resulting in the loss of a hangar, two ships and a crew led to the desertion of the Belgian Zeppelin bases; LZ-39 was transferred east. Not forgetting their heavy losses of 1914, the Army was becoming concerned that 1915 would set a similar record. Their senior captain, Alfred Horn, had lost Z-10 to French gunnery in March, and in May both LZ-34 and LZ-35 fell victims to ground artillery over the western front. June had been disastrous. Other than a single sortie by L-10 over Tyneside in the middle of the month, the Navy had seen fit to lie low for the time being.

Thanks to the short summer nights, Britain remained unmolested right through to 9th August when Strasser despactched five ships, four of them with orders to harass London while Odo Loewe in L-9 went north to repeat earlier successful raids on the industrial areas. A single Zeppelin could paralyse night work without dropping any bombs. The rest of the squadron was in trouble from the start. Mathy pulled out with engine trouble within sight of the coast, and again due to poor visibility, not one of the ships located the City. Despite the fact that all the commanders were Germany's best, their navigational efforts were reduced to guesswork as was evident by their inaccurate reports. On the way home, the Dover guns blew a big hole in Peterson's L-12, which came down in the sea. It was successfully towed into Ostend but there it blew up as it was being lifted out of the water by crane.

After the fiasco of mid-June, the Army left Britain alone for the rest of the year, but the Navy continued its attacks intermittently through to 13th October.

The sudden storms of the North Sea were the reasons for the reduction in bombing raids during the last three months of 1915. Few reconnaissance flights were made during that time, largely because of the hazards of moving ships out of and back into their sheds. Why the Germans never used mooring masts seems not to have been answered. Britain had even provided one for the *Mayfly* in 1911, while in 1917 the original and long-lasting high mast at Pulham in Norfolk came into service.

During the raidless three months the strength of the Zeppelin forces increased, eight new ships having been produced during this spell, five being allotted to the Navy in the group L-17 to L-21 inclusive. Despite the build-up, crews were fretting because of delays to the new "R type" giants of two million cubic feet, caused by lack of space in the existing assembly halls. There being no alternative, the manufacturers cleverly began to stretch the "P type" by the insertion of an extra 50-foot section which added 138,000 cubic feet to the volume, 2½ tons to the lift and 1,500 feet to the existing 11,000-feet altitude. These most useful hybrids were the "Q type" and of the fifteen built, five went to the Navy as L-20 to L-24 inclusive between Christmas, 1915, and May, 1916. Only nine days after the delivery of L-24 the first of the long-cherished "R types" came along on 28th May, 1916.

Although the gunnery defences of Britain had been expanding steadily and in many ways gave a very good account of themselves, that which finally broke the Zeppelin campaign was the expansion and consolidation of the Aeroplane Barrage Line. This was a 500-mile line of defences stretching from Edinburgh to the south coast, the primary units being some thirty aerodromes allotted to the R.F.C. Home Defence squadrons. The line began at Turnhouse, ten miles west of Edinburgh, and followed the east coast to Hartlepool, the last of five stations on that section being at Seaton Carew. Between Turnhouse and Seaton Carew some two dozen searchlight stations gave support to patrolling pilots, master control centres at Newcastle and Hartlepool providing the essential link. The defence line started again inland at Catterick and traced a swerving but unbroken aerial fence right through the middle of England to London, where it spread out into Hertfordshire and Essex. Air defence was also well concentrated between Norwich and King's Lynn and in the area between Dover and Tunbridge Wells. The strategic catchnet of the whole system was the string of coastal stations operated by the Royal Naval Air Service, who were responsible for trying to intercept raiders both on their first approach and afterwards during their return to Germany.

In the middle of 1915 Lord Kitchener took the R.F.C. to task for not being more effective in deterring the Zeppelins, even though the responsibility actually still rested on the Admiralty and despite the fact that demands from France left virtually only instructors and pupils in the U.K.

The transfer of reponsibility from the Admiralty to the War Office in 1915 took months to resolve while the R.F.C. was reorganising its commitments. The reorganisation became effective in February, 1916, spearheaded by the air defence of London being placed under the inspired leadership of Major T. C. R. Higgins, whose efforts were largely responsible for his pilots defeating the Zeppelins in the attacks of September, 1916. From his headquarters at Hounslow Heath he directed the operations of his patrols based on a ring of aerodromes around London at Croydon, Farningham, Hornchurch, Hainault, Hendon, Chingford and Northolt. By April 15th, 1916, it was possible for Major Higgins to look with some pride on his handiwork as No. 39 Squadron (Home Defence), soon to become the elite of Zeppelin-killer squadrons, came into formal existence. In May, 1916, he split his squadron into three flights of six aircraft, one flight taking up quarters at each of the three aerodromes of Hornchurch, Hainault and North Weald Bassett. A close rival for the defence against the London raiders was No. 37 Squadron, operating out of Essex aerodromes at Woodham Mortimer, Rochford, Stow Maries and Goldhanger.

No. 33 Squadron had formed up in Lincolnshire under Major Thomson, No. 36 at Newcastle under Major Marsh, No. 50 in Kent under Major Christie, and No. 51 in Norfolk under Major Wylie. Other squadrons such as No. 75 near Cardington followed after the critical September, but before the end of 1916.

When raiding was resumed on January 31st, 1916, instead of two undersized and underpowered airships, each with a warload of half a ton, there were nine ships, each carrying about two and a half tons. If anything, the weather was worse than before, with freezing fog being widespread except where snow and sleet was falling heavily. The flagship was von Buttlar's L-11 carrying Strasser who was actively directing and leading the raid, as he had tried to do one year earlier.

With the increased range of the new ships, raids began to involve deep penetration into enemy territory; average flight time for all ships was in excess of twenty hours. The area covered by this raid encompassed the whole of the industrial Midlands, and most of the ships spent a considerable time in the target zones. Very few of the bigger industrial cities escaped attention from the raiders, despite the fact that it was one of the worst nights on record for the number of engine failures. Fanning out but unable to make much height, they took in Leicester, Birmingham and Liverpool, across to Manchester, Sheffield and Hull, with Burton-on-Trent being hit several times during the night. The disruption to industry was obviously great and the toll of death and injury was heavy, with more than seventy killed and over a hundred injured.

After the raid, L-19 was in a precarious condition, having been in constant difficulties with engine trouble. Around dawn, Loewe coaxed his ship back in the general direction of Germany but at their nearest point to home neutral Dutch coastal gunners opened fire on them and drove them back out to sea. With only one of four engines functioning and with a strong southerly wind blowing, L-19 drifted out of sight of land and finally and very slowly sank into the North Sea. The story of how the water logged hull was discovered the following day by the Grimsby trawler *King Stephen* has been told with minor variations in all the many Zeppelin histories written to date. All relate how the skipper spoke with the crew of L-19 but despite their entreaties left them to drown. When the German authorities later received messages contained in bottles washed up on Scandinavian shores they had sufficient facts to mount a world-wide anti-British campaign.

An historian of a later age, Colin Walker, news editor of the *Grimsby Evening Telegraph*, reasearched the story of the *King Stephen* and besides interviewing two surviving members of the original crew, the Burret brothers, delved into Admiralty archives. A brief extract from Walker's very comprehensive account in two successive issues of his newspaper in March, 1964, relates how the trawler skipper

"refused to take the survivors on board, on the grounds that they could overpower her crew and take the trawler back to Germany. Instead, skipper 'Mad Brummie' Martin steamed off to find a bigger ship capable of accommodating the Germans in safety. Skipper Martin's report to the guardship at the mouth of the Humber sent patrol vessels racing off into the North Sea to pick up the airmen, but they were never found. In the position given by Skipper Martin, nothing was found to suggest that a Zeppelin had ever been there — no bodies — no wreckage — nothing!

"The question was, what happened in the North Sea on February 2nd, 1916, the day the *King Stephen* sighted the Zeppelin? In Grimsby, the naval authorities pressed their investigation of Skipper Martin's report and turned up the astonishing fact that he had deliberately given an incorrect position for the Zeppelin.

"The plain truth was that Martin had been fishing in a prohibited zone of the North Sea, the Cleaver Bank. The naval staff monograph states . . . 'The *King Stephen* steamed off to find a patrol boat, the shouts of the Germans to be saved dying away in the distance, but it was not until she reached the Humber in the morning of February 3rd, 1916, that she found any vessel to receive her report. Even then, her skipper gave the wrong position. He had been fishing in a prohibited area and did not wish to incriminate himself . . .'
"The position he gave was 40 miles short of that of the Zeppelin, the one in which Martin should have been fishing!"

After this, activity by the Naval airships again ceased for several weeks, but in the meantime the Army crews were very much occupied on both the eastern and western fronts. In particular, the Zeppelins were being used to augment the assaults being made on Verdun, with the result that LZ-79 was lost on 31st January and LZ-95 and LZ-77 on 22nd February.

By early March, Naval Zeppelins were renewing their operations, due partly to a more aggressive outlook on the part of Admiral Scheer, who had replaced von Pohl. Hoping to learn more of the dispositions of Jellicoe's Fleet and also to use the Zeppelins as bait to lure odd British naval units into the path of German flotillas, Scheer began to employ his airships more strategically. On 5th March L-11, L-13 and L-14 were sent out in an attempt to reconnoitre important British naval bases in Scotland. Severe blizzards limited their efforts to a sporadic bombing of parts of Yorkshire.

As Strasser began preparing his spring offensive, little did he know that Major Higgins at Hounslow was grooming his own resources for the not-too-distant dispersal and destruction of those same Zeppelins.

Beginning on 31st March with a full-scale squadron raid, nine raids were made by 2nd May. On the first occasion, L-15 was badly damaged by gunfire near Dartford and later, while well out into the Thames Estuary, was further attacked by an aeroplane of No. 39 Squadron from Hainault Farm near Ilford, flown by Second Lieutenant A. de B. Brandon. Gas losses forced L-15 down into the sea, where Breithaupt and his crew, with a single exception, were fortunate enough to survive and become prisoners of war.

On 2nd May a force of eight Zeppelins set out to locate and attack British vessels at Rosyth in the Firth of Forth. Due to strong headwinds developing during the course of the flight, six of the airship commanders turned away and went for alternative targets. Two held on for the north, Böcker with L-14 and Stabbert with L-20, both ships encountering really foul weather, with a heavy layer of snow and ice on the envelopes. L-14 went well past the Firth of Forth before turning away for Germany but Stabbert made serious mistakes and L-20 went as far north as the Orkneys before aiming for Norway.

By the following noon, Stabbert was within sight of land but L-20 was nearly out of fuel and he tried making a forced landing on the Norwegian coast. L-20 finally splashed down in a fiord near Stavanger and a wet, frozen and much relieved crew cheerfully submitted to internment.

No further raids occurred for nearly two months. On the other hand, the historic Battle of Jutland which took place at the end of May should have given the Zeppelins their ultimate opportunity of proving their worth, but they scarcely justified their existence.

Possibly the most important result stemming from the presence of Zeppelins at Jutland was the effect on British naval morale and, hence, on later airship policies. As late as January, 1917, Admiral Sir David Beatty was making bitter complaints about not having big scouting rigids in service with the Royal Navy.

Once again, the short midsummer nights brought a lull in the raids on Britain, which were not resumed until the end of July. Many new developments were taking place in the meantime, among them being the deployment of commandeered trawlers armed with high-angle guns along the well-known Zeppelin routes as advanced warning stations. At the same time as new strategies, new tactics and new weapons were all being brought to bear on the Zeppelin threat, the new and very advanced "R type" Zeppelins came into service.

By an extension in length of 65 feet and in diameter of 17 feet, the volume of the new "Super Zeppelin" increased to almost two million cubic feet and thus raised the Useful Lift from the 39,000 pounds of the "Q type" to a new high of 62,000 pounds for L-30, the prototype, and of 72,000 pounds in later specimens. Such ships were by August, 1916, carrying bomb loads of around four tons, a very appreciable advance. The supplement of two more engines in separate wing-cars, besides giving a slight increase in speed, was effective in offsetting engine failures.

British agents had reported the anticipated launching of what they described as a "Super Zeppelin" and when it first appeared at Friedrichshafen neutral observers described it as such. Though the works serial was LZ-62, at this point the Navy began its own new series of service numbers by making it L-30. Commissioned on 30th May, it was flown to Nordholz by the late crew of the L-11 under von Buttlar.

The Navy got its second ship of this kind, L-31, by mid-July, its third one, L-32, by 4th August, and its fourth one, L-33, by 2nd September. The Navy were now getting all the best ships and the Army had to wait until the following February. The Army at this time was conducting a sporadic campaign in Bulgaria and around Salonika, where it lost LZ-85 to the gunners of H.M.S. *Agamemnon*. A few Army ships still remained close to the western front and occasionally raided Paris and London.

August, 1916, saw Navy Zeppelins involved in increasing attempts to harass Britain with heavier and more frequent night-raiding. In the eyes of British Intelligence, it was clearly the beginning of an all-out onslaught making use of the longer winter nights and the bigger and more plentiful airships.

Experienced pilots realised they could never win just as long as everything depended on their getting the advantage of height; despite general orders to carry bombs, unofficially and quietly some left them off and concentrated more on the efficiency of their aeroplanes and guns. Much was made possible by dedicated teams

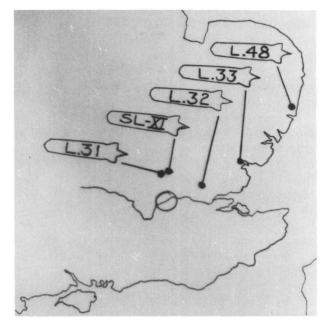

Map showing the location of five Zeppelins destroyed over Britain during the First World War.

L-31 Potters Bar
      2nd October, 1916

L-32 Billericay
      24th September, 1916

L-33 Wigborough
      24th September, 1916

L-48 Theberton
      17th June, 1917

SL-11 Cuffley
      3rd September, 1916

of mechanics. The loading of ammunition pans for Lewis guns was largely at the discretion of individual pilots, but generally these were loaded with a mixture of tracers, incendiaries and explosive bullets, which since 1914 had been under development for a variety of uses by a variety of people, each with different ideas. The magnesium tracer, known to pilots as "Sparklet", was developed at Woolwich Arsenal while the incendiary known as "Buckingham" was a flat-nosed phosphorus bullet produced by a civilian engineer of that name at Coventry. Both types had varying degrees of success when used against static balloons, and both had several limitations. The third, well tried and used, was the Brock explosive invented by a naval officer of that name. The Pomeroy P.S.A., first evolved in 1914 by the Australian John Pomeroy, was an explosive type too sensitive to gain the confidence of pilots pressing the trigger. Pomeroy had a factory in Acton where development work was carried out to make it safer. He planned to hand over the .303-inch cylinders of evil to the War Office on 2nd September, and it was Captain Leefe-Robinson to whom the ammunition was given for the first trials in active service that same night.

The biggest fleet of Zeppelins ever to attempt to raid England had set out from Germany early on the afternoon of Saturday, 2nd September, twelve Naval ships and four Army ships. Early wireless activity ruined any German idea of it being a surprise attack and the British defence system was on the alert hours before the invaders were seen or heard.

51

Individual ships raided around Grimsby and Hull while Ernst Lehmann in LZ-98 came in from Belgium, followed the coast from Deal to Dungeness, headed inland via Ashford and Maidstone and finally dropped his bomb load at Gravesend. LZ-90, commanded by la Quiante, came in near Clacton and was soon in trouble with its rarely used Spybasket which it managed to jettison at Mistley, north of Colchester, before dropping bombs at Haverhill. It passed over Lavenham, Suffolk, just before 1 a.m. and Pulham, Norfolk, half an hour later, then headed out to sea over Great Yarmouth. Kurt Frankenberg in L-21 came in at Cromer and, cruising steadily past Norwich and Cambridge, reached Bedford at about 2 a.m. and performed an abrupt turn about, curiously enough exactly above Cardington, and then flew in a great circle over south Bedfordshire, dropping several bombs near Biggleswade. It was finally plotted as being at King's Lynn at 3.40 a.m. and dropped the remainder of its bomb load from there through Sandringham to the coast which it left at Hunstanton at 4 a.m.

These apparently erratic flight paths show how the general intention of the raid was to saturate the countryside everywhere and to inflict the maximum disruption and fear. The one ship that especially commands our attention is the Army's Schutte-Lanz SL-11. Commanded by the London-born Wilhelm Schramm, whose father had worked for the Siemens company, SL-11 was of the new "E type" of 1½ million cubic feet capacity. Its bomb load of 6,300 pounds exceeded that of any of the other ships flying that night, including the two new "R type" Zeppelins L-30 and L-32. Coming in over Foulness at 10.40 p.m., SL-11 passed slightly to the east of Witham and Braintree, struggling to gain height before heading for London. The ship circled Saffron Walden at 11.35 p.m., changed course at Royston at 12.20 a.m. and headed for Hitchin and Luton without having dropped bombs. After passing over St Albans, Schramm took a few sighting shots with small bombs and commenced

This photograph from the archives of his old squadron, No. 39, believed not to have been published before, shows Captain Leefe-Robinson in his BE 12, with his mechanics displaying parts of the airship shot down the night before. *Commanding Officer, No. 39 Squadron*

weaving, presumably in an attempt to deflect the searchlights and guns of the outer London defence area.

Squadrons in the Home Counties flew off their standing patrols at about 11 p.m., giving them about three-quarters of an hour to reach cruise altitude along clearly defined lines which, if crossed by an intruder, would probably lead to an interception. No. 39 Squadron's three aeroplanes from North Weald, Hainault and Sutton's Farm, whose pilots were rapidly becoming veterans, took off for their patrol lines. After two hours, a second trio was despatched as a reinforcement and replacement since each aircraft carried fuel supplies for three hours. Among the pilots airborne that night was Captain Leefe-Robinson. Leefe-Robinson's report of his action that night has become a classic of air history:

"... I climbed to 10,000 feet in 53 minutes ... I saw nothing till 1.10 a.m. when two searchlights picked up a Zeppelin about SE of Woolwich. The clouds had collected in this quarter and the searchlights had some difficulty in keeping on the aircraft. By this time, I had managed to climb to 12,900 feet and I made in the direction of the Zeppelin which was being fired on by a few anti-aircraft guns—hoping to cut if off on its way eastward. I very slowly gained on it for about ten minutes—I judged it to be about 800 feet below me and I sacrificed my speed in order to keep the height. It went behind some clouds, avoiding the searchlights, and I lost sight of it. After fifteen minutes of fruitless search, I returned to my patrol. I managed to pick up and distinguish my flares again. At about 1.50 a.m. I noticed a red glow in NE London. Taking it to be an outbreak of fire I went in that direction. At 2.5 a.m. a Zeppelin was picked up by searchlights over NNE London, as far as I could judge ...

"Remembering my last failure I sacrificed height (I was still 12,900 feet) for speed and made nose down in the direction of the Zeppelin. I saw shells bursting and night tracer shells flying around it. When I drew closer I noticed that the anti-aircraft aim was too high or too low; also a good many some 800 feet behind—a few tracers went right over. I could hear the bursts when about 3,000 feet from the Zeppelin. I flew about 800

Hauptmann Wilhelm Schramm, seated second left, and the crew of the SL-11, brought down at Cuffley, Hertfordshire, on 3rd September, 1916, by Captain Leefe-Robinson. *Kurt Puzicha*

Kapitän-Leutnant Werner Peterson and the crew of L-32, destroyed at Billericay by Lieutenant F. Sowrey, of No. 39 Squadron, on 24th September, 1916. The same crew had earlier survived being shot down into the Channel in L-12. This photograph was supplied by Mrs. Hutzli, of New York, sister of Frederick Heider, who is seen on the extreme right, marked with a cross.

feet below it from bow to stern and distributed one drum along it (alternate Brock and Pomeroy), it seemed to have no effect. I therefore moved to one side and gave it another drum, distributed along its side—without apparent effect.

"I then got behind it (by this time I was very close—500 feet or less) and concentrated one drum on one part (underneath rear). I was then at a height of 11,500 feet when attacking Zeppelin. I hardly finished the drum before I saw the part fired at glow. In a few seconds the whole rear part was blazing."

The ship thus destroyed was SL-11, which crashed on the Ridgeway at Cuffley, behind the Plough Inn, a nearby memorial to Leefe Robinson marking the place where Schramm and his crew were all killed.

The effect on British morale was almost unbelievable, and Robinson's award of the Victoria Cross was well earned and doubtless the least the public would have accepted.

Widespread looting of souvenir scraps of the SL-11 wreckage, which obstructed Admiralty and War Office technicians seeking information of airship technology,

Turning back from over the Thames Estuary in a crippled condition, the L-33 was landed by Böcker and his crew with great skill in the darkness of a September night. After ensuring the safety of the occupants of a nearby farmhouse, Böcker set fire to his ship and then marched his crew up the lane after inquiring at George Rout's cottage as to the way to Colchester.   *George Rout*

caused considerable official concern. Consequently, magistrates were ordered to inflict deterrent fines, while the police and military everywhere were under orders to mount guard over any new wrecks with the utmost alacrity.

Three weeks after the pillage of SL-11, a fleet of twelve Naval Zeppelins set out on another raid on 23rd September. Four of the twelve were the almost new L-30, L-31, L-32 and L-33. As on the previous occasion, the rapidly improving Home Defence organisation moved swiftly and smoothly into action. Robinson's squadron colleague Frederick Sowrey soon found himself led to his target, like Robinson, by the activity of searchlights and anti-aircraft batteries. This time it was Werner Peterson in L-32 who was in trouble as Sowrey, after several minutes of desperate manoeuvering in the thin air at 13,000 feet to hold on to his target, poured in three drums of the deadly Brock and Pomeroy, resulting in the start of another holocaust.

The burning L-32 threatened to fall on the town of Billericay, but it slanted across the inhabited parts during the last stages of its fall, shedding an elevator in the process, and finally spread its remains across the open fields of Snails Hall Farm at Great Burstead.

What seemed incredible to many of the still cheering crowds was the appearance within minutes of a similar blood-red glow in the night sky. Twenty-five miles away, L-33 was burning furiously on the ground at Little Wigborough, just behind Mersea Island, Essex. Six months earlier, L-15 had been damaged by London's anti-aircraft guns and later by an attack from a Be 2c flown by Lieutenant Brandon, and now L-33 had experienced an almost identical circumstance, except that Captain Böcker managed to turn back in time to make an extremely skilful forced landing in complete safety. After considerately warning the occupants of an adjacent farmhouse, he deliberately fired the ship by burning his papers in the control-car.

Half a century afterwards, the author discovered George Rout, living in the same cottage from which he had witnessed the end of the L-33 when he was a

14-year-old boy. He recalled hearing a knock on the door and there stood the Captain, while the twenty-one crew waited patiently and correctly nearby. Having asked the direction to take for Colchester, the Zeppelin commander brought his men smartly to attention and marched them in good order towards the nearby village of Peldon. Being a remote and thinly populated region, the wreck was almost immune from looters and the crew safe from mobs wanting to lynch them. They were met by Special Constable Edgar Nicholas on his bicycle, who led them to the Post Office at Peldon. The party was joined on the way by Sergeant Edwards of the Metropolitan Police, who was off duty and in civilian clothes. At Peldon, Sergeant Smith of the Essex Police took charge, and after relieving the crew of their sidearms, telephoned the military on Mersea Island for an escort to collect the prisoners.

Fifty-seven years later, I spent two days in Hamburg with Peter Morsdorf, the one-time wireless operator of L-33, now the only survivor. He recalled that at first they were confined very comfortably in the Church Hall at West Mersea and later taken to Colchester and then to an hotel in London. Some of the specialist technical crewmen were taken back to the wreck to help explain the functioning of unusual items of equipment. In due course, the crewmen were sent up north to the P.O.W. camp at Stobs in southern Scotland and the officers to Donington Hall in Leicestershire.

British technologists could scarcely believe their good fortune when they examined the wreckage in daylight, successfully fenced in and protected by a massive military cordon. The wreck lay across two fields, straddling Copt Hall Lane. Other than cutting a hole through the centre for farm vehicles, they allowed it to lie undisturbed for three months with nobody allowed near without a military pass, despite the arrival of crowds estimated at nearly a quarter of a million people.

Lieutenant-Commander A. P. Cole, of the Royal Corps of Naval Constructors,

Opposite: Alloys Böcker and the crew of L-33 pose before the new "R-type" Zeppelin, which was only three weeks old when it crashed-landed in Essex. Peter Morsdorf is at the back, arrowed.   *Peter Morsdorf*

Right: Nearly half a century later, the irrepressible Peter Morsdorf hurries to greet the author during a visit to Hamburg in 1973.   *Author*

was given the vital task of evaluating the wreck of L-33. He took up residence at Wigborough with a hand-picked team of Admiralty draughtsmen and engineers, and throughout the winter recorded every feature of the L-33, by far the least damaged of the newest "R type" Zeppelins to fall into British hands. By February, 1917, the work had been completed and published as the secret CB1265, the drawings of which enabled British constructors to produce the near-replica airships R-33 and R-34, probably the two most successful ships ever made in Britain. As Cole expressed it in writing to the author: "Had it not been for the German Zeppelin L-33 being brought down in Essex, I doubt that we would have progressed very far. Sutcliffe, May and I were immediately sent down to the wreck and, together with all the draughtsmen, were able to make detailed drawings of the structure and 'reconstruct' the complete ship. The main problem confronting us was the correct tensioning of the bracing wires. I ultimately solved this problem, for which I received the M.B.E." This latter remark may well astonish the reader for its apparent disproportionate reward, until it is understood that this may well have been the first time anyone had solved the complex stressing of the world's biggest birdcage, long before the age of the computer.

The L-33 was the third big new rigid to have been lost to the Germans in as many weeks. Predictably, the few raids that followed were very half-hearted; on 1st October, 1916, only seven of the eleven ships that set out from Germany actually crossed the English coastline, and only one made a really determined effort to break through to London. This was the L-31, commanded by the famous Heinrich Mathy, which crossed the coast near Lowestoft. After passing Hertford, L-31 came under the concentrated fire of the North London guns and was held fast by their searchlights, which quickly attracted the attention of patrolling British interceptor pilots.

One of these was Second Lieutenant W. J. Tempest, of the now celebrated No. 39 Squadron. Tempest was well ahead of three other pilots, all of whom were racing full throttle to join combat with the raider before he could escape. When Mathy discovered the extent of his danger he sought desperately to climb out of reach, jettisoning six 660-pound bombs in and around Cheshunt. Despite his amazing rate of climb, he failed to escape from Tempest and the L-31 fell blazing from 12,000 feet on to the eastern edge of Oakmere Park, Potters Bar.

Kapitän-Leutnant Heinrich Mathy and the crew of the L-31, destroyed at Potters Bar on 2nd October, 1916, by Second Lieutenant W. J. Tempest, of No. 39 Squadron.   *Kurt Puzicha*

CHAPTER SIX

Through Adversity to Airships

THIS parody of the Royal Air Force motto "Per Ardua ad Astra" fits well into the history of the British rigid airship. Scarcely can one find a parallel in British technological industries of a major product of unique character that suffered so much by being the pawn of successive political factions.

The next British rigid after the *Mayfly*, No.9, took until the end of November, 1916, to make its first flight. Even worse, it was so far removed from its original minimum performance specification that it took another six months of intensive modification work before the Admiralty accepted it from the builders.

In No. 9, the four engines were mounted as pairs in each of the two main cars, with massive extension shaft drives to swivelling propellers intended to improve the take-off and landing. The overall length of 526 feet and the diameter of 53 feet provided the ship with a nominal gas capacity of 866,000 cubic feet in seventeen cells. As originally built, the Useful Lift was well below the specified 7,000 pounds and it was not until the two rear engines had been replaced by a single and more powerful Maybach from the wrecked L-33 that this improved.

Some idea of how seriously we were behind the Germans can be had by comparing No.9 with the German Z-12 of 1914, of about the same size. Z-12 could better No.9's 40 m.p.h. by 10 m.p.h. while No.9's Useful Lift was more than trebled at 27,000 pounds.

Nevertheless, No.9, under its commander E. A. D. Masterman, has its place in history as the first British rigid to fly. During its flying life of just under 200 hours it helped Wallis, Masterman and Scott to develop the high mooring mast at Pulham and acted as a training ship for future air and ground crews. To have trained in No.9 was to be highly esteemed and among those so trained were Hunt and Greenstreet, who became Chief Cox'ns of the R.101 and R.100 respectively.

Early in 1915, twenty-four young sub-lieutenants and midshipmen were selected from the crews of battleships at Scapa Flow and ordered to report to the Admiralty in London. There, Admiral Fisher personally briefed them; they were to man small non-rigid airships being constructed at such frantic pace that ordinary aeroplane fuselages were being harnessed to pressure-type envelopes without waiting for properly designed gondolas. Admiral Fisher made it perfectly clear that their duty was to master the U-boats or die in the attempt.

This was one of several factors to make 1915 one of the most politically critical years in the history of British airships. Churchill as First Lord of the Admiralty from August, 1911, until May, 1915, when he was unseated by a change of government, had been involved in a constant struggle for power with Admiral Fisher, the First Sea

Lord. Fisher wanted lighter-than-air craft, Churchill did not, so airship developments were deprived of necessary political support. The rigid was revived after Balfour took over but it took months to get things going again. As rigid development resumed, Fisher's SS type non-rigids arrived, giving their crews almost two years of priceless experience before the rigids came into service. Incidentally, the SS type did succeed in mastering the U-boat menace in so far as no ship or convoy was ever attacked while an airship was in sight.

A specialised committee, originated by Balour, recommended increased production of rigids, but Vickers were still the only company with the necessary experience and facilities. The Admiralty wanted another three airships, bigger than No.9. To stretch the existing design was all very well, but with Vickers as builders, size was limited to that of their assembly hall, a mere nine feet longer than No.9.

In October, 1915, drawings were approved and contracts allotted for one new ship each at Vickers, Beardmore, and Armstrong Whitworth. By December, another sixteen ships had been budgeted for, all of them to be of the "23 class" (as the stretched "9's" were called.) Shorts then came on to the "Approved List of Constructors" and immediately existing contracts were revised to give each builder three ships. Contracts were one thing, but the building of the huge new sheds ran into trouble due to the rest of industry competing for priority in the supply of raw materials. Vickers themselves tried to help by making extra batches of airship components for the newcomers as well as providing many of the steel girders required for the new sheds. Until these had been built, no-one could assemble the new ships other than Vickers, who were supposed to be getting a new large shed, 365 feet longer at 900 feet. This considerable extension applied only to Vickers, and the other manufacturers had to be content with sheds of a uniform 700 feet.

In the event, the new Vickers shed incurred so much trouble of various kinds that it was never completed. It was unfortunate that experience gained at Vickers

Britain's first rigid airship commander, Wing Commander E. A. D. Masterman, third from right in the front row, with the trials crew of H.M.A. No. 9. The civilian sitting next to him is the chief designer, H. B. Pratt, and the civilian sitting towards the left is the works manager, James Watson.   *David Cook*

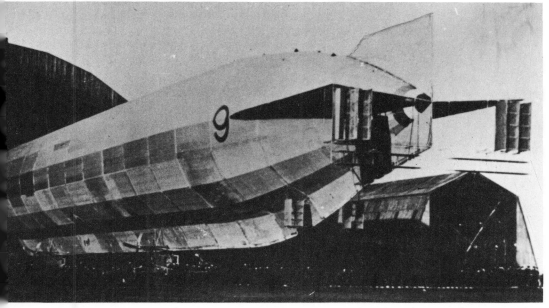

H.M.A. No. 9 emerges from her assembly shed at Barrow. To the right is the waterside structure where the *Mayfly* was built. *H. G. Parker*

could not be fully exploited because of this handicap; in retrospect it is easy to appreciate what a frustration this posed for the talented young Barnes Wallis.

In early 1916 four constructors held contracts, while a tremendous shed building programme surged ahead. At this period, Captain Murray F. Sueter, Superintendent of Aircraft Construction at the Admiralty, instituted the new airship design group recruited from the Royal Corps of Naval Constructors, under the general supervision of Commander C. I. R. Campbell. No longer would airship design remain the monopoly of the Vickers organisation, with the Royal Navy having little more than a customer's representative status. For the future, it would be Admiralty policy to advance its own knowledge of the art and to utilise its own naval architects to determine requirement specifications. From there, they would progress by stages with the avowed intent of establishing a Royal Airship Works where both design and construction would eventually come under their total control.

Shorts were told to ignore every known existing design and to prepare themselves for a completely new project, to be constructed in wood, the general layout for which would be coming to them direct from an Admiralty department. Their responsibility would be to carry out the detail design work and to build the structure in their Cardington premises under the supervision of Admiralty overseers.

Clearly this was the thin edge of the wedge, and Cardington became the prime target for consolidating Admiralty policy. The late Lieutenant-Commander A. P. Cole, a lifelong naval architect and designer of the *Kelly*-class destroyers, had been appointed to airship duties during this period and, in a letter to the author, explained the situation as follows . . .

"A separate department called Director of Production (Airships) or DP(A) was formed in 1917 and no fewer than eight members of the R.C.N.C. were detailed to form the Technical Branch. They consisted of

S. E. Boyland	Chief Constructor
C. I. R. Campbell	Constructor
A. P. Cole ⎫ F. Sutcliffe ⎬ H. May ⎭	Assistant Constructors to form the Design Staff
S. Payne	Overseer at Cardington
H. B. W. Evans	Overseer at Barrow
L. Bartlett	Overseer at Renfrew (Inchinnan)

"Boyland was specially promoted to Chief Constructor to take over the Airship Section, but I think he found that Campbell was too much of a handfull and he rapidly faded from the scene. The domineering character was Campbell, and since we had all been trained as Naval Architects we knew absolutely nothing about airship design or construction or even of aerodynamics. The design staff, with draughtsmen and the necessary clerical staff, was located at 10 Smith Square, Westminster.
"Since our correspondence started, I have thought a lot about our rigid airship programmes and what I now consider should have been done. There is no doubt that the German rigid airship design was a masterpiece of light structural development and there was only one man in this country who could have equalled Dr Eckener in ingenuity in this type of construction and that was Barnes Wallis. It was a mistake placing the responsibility for airship design with Naval Architects—the order should have gone to Vickers at Barrow, by whom Wallis was employed."

The administrative aims thus depicted by Cole were never to reach 100% fulfilment, due to the termination of Britain's naval airship activities in 1921. On the other hand, the pressures exerted in pursuance of those aims did have a number of different results on each of the companies concerned, mostly in the way in which Admiralty demands overcame the proposals or alternatives of their civilian counterparts.

Cardington was singled out for special attention almost before the factory was built. Shorts had in fact been given two new airship serial numbers, R.31 and R.32, numbers which they had fully expected they would be using against allocations of ships in the "23 class". The Admiralty were determined to keep Cardington production facilities free of any of this blockage.

H.M.A. No.9 from Vickers had already taken three years to materialise and, overweight as it was, it took until the spring of 1917 before it could be accepted into

Naval Architect Charles Ivor Rae Campbell at Cardington. A zealous Scot and the architect of the Royal Airship works as an ideal and almost a faith, Campbell died in the R.38 disaster in 1921, generally accepted as a tragedy of his own making.

H. G. Parker

service, obsolete and virtually useless except as a trainer. This was at exactly the time the Shorts factory was due for completion, and here the Admiralty saw the prospect of putting more advanced projects into construction rather than just adding to the number of "23 class" ships still to come.

The number on order was reduced when it was found how great was the gap between their performance and that of the newest German ships. Furthermore, under Admiralty pressure, major modifications were introduced into the last few "23 class" ships being constructed. The actual and final build figures produced the following results.

Vickers	No.23 September, 1917	R.26 March, 1918
Beardmore	No.24 October, 1917	R.27 June, 1918
Armstrong Whitworth	No.25 October, 1917	R.29 June, 1918

The first four ships of the "23 class" were of a uniform 940,000 cubic feet displacement in 18 gas cells, whereas R.27 and R.29 had been modified to 990,600 cubic feet and had their external keels deleted and an internal walking corridor built within the structure of the hull. These two ships were designated as being of the "23X class".

All six of the ships had four engines in three engine-cars driving six propellers. Each of the forward and after cars carried a single engine driving twin propellers while the centre car carried two engines, each one driving its own propeller.

The engines, unlike the side-valve six-cylinder Wolseley-Maybach of No.9,

Above: The forward car of H.M.A. No. 23.
Royal Aeronautical Society

Left: An in-flight photograph of tests on the swivelling propellers of H.M.A. No. 9.   *H. G. Parker*

Below: Last of the "23 Series" was R.29, built by Armstrong Whitworth at Selby and seen here at East Fortune undergoing experiments on fabrics and dopes and aerofoil tests by the National Physical Laboratory. *Mr S. Duke*

were the much larger Rolls Royce Eagle V-12 engines, fore-runners of the Merlin. Those fitted to the early "23 class" were the Series 3 of about 280 h.p., while the Series 6 of over 300 h.p. were fitted in the "23X" ships. Numerous machinery installation experiments were applied, some at Pulham, some at Howden, and some at East Fortune. As with No.9, certain of L-33's Maybach engines went into individual ships of the "23" and "23X class", complete with their original, but repaired, power cars.

Maximum speed of all the ships in these series was about 50/55 m.p.h. and Useful Lift Values varied from ship to ship, being as little as five tons for the first one built and nine tons for the last one. All were scrapped in 1919 (other than R.27, already destroyed in a spectacular fire in the Howden hangars in 1918).

These ships were soon a familiar sight all over Britain, and most of them flew some 2–300 flying hours apiece. R.29 logged over 400 hours and was the only British rigid ever to go into combat action against the enemy. On 29th September, 1918, off the Northumberland coast, R.29 flying from East Fortune was escorting a merchant convoy out of Hull when an oil-slick was spotted, indicating the probable presence of a U-boat manoeuvring for attack. R.29 dropped bombs and called up Royal Navy ships while she continued to overfly the area, ensuring that the target should not slip away unobserved. After the Navy had maintained its attack for two days and nights it was established that UB-115, just out from Zeebrugge on its maiden voyage, had been destroyed.

This one attack on a submarine represents the total war achievements of the British rigid airship, despite its being originated as early as 1908. This poor record is testimony to the intermittent breaks in political support which prevented any consistent development work. The delivery programme of the "23s" was such that even these very inadequate airships only came into service during the closing few months of the war, and it was 1917 before plans were being put into action to give the Navy anything better, though this entailed nothing more than building separate German designs, already becoming outdated. In the event, neither of the two designs came into service before the war came to an end on 11th November, 1918.

The excellent retrieval work by Lieutenant-Commander Cole of the design of the "R type" Zeppelin was completed by the spring of 1917, just as Shorts' Cardington facility became functional; in theory, Cardington could well have been set to work almost immediately on the Anglicised versions of the L-33. Instead, this work was allotted to the northern factories of Beardmore at Inchinnan on the Clyde and Armstrong Whitworth at Selby in Yorkshire. Manufacture of components for R.33 and R.34 began in the summer of 1917, but first H.M.A. 24 at Beardmore and H.M.A. 25 at Armstrong Whitworth had to be delivered in October before the second cradles could be vacated for the assembly of the new ships alongside the R.27 at Beardmore and R.29 at Armstrong Whitworth. The R.27 and R.29 did not themselves reach delivery stage until June, 1918, and R.33 and R.34 did not fly until 1919.

The latter ships and others being programmed were to be known as the "33 class", which in fact had no more connection with the German L-33 than sheer coincidence, the prototype serial R.33 being in straight sequence after the allocation of the numbers R.31 and R.32 to Cardington.

It was at this stage that the misfortunes of Vickers at Barrow fell upon the shoulders of Barnes Wallis; none of the new ships could be allotted to them because of the failure of the shed building programme to give Vickers the bigger sizes needed. Cardington, with its new 700-feet twin-berth shed, ready in April, 1917, could have dealt with the new type, but the "33s" were not put in there because the space was already spoken for. In fact, Chief Draughtsman Claude Lipscomb and his team had already been making substantial progress in the town of Bedford, well before the Cardington establishment was ready to receive them.

The origins of the design being worked on in Bedford stemmed from layouts smuggled into Britain from the Schutte-Lanz Company of Mannheim in Germany. The individual involved is said to have been a Swiss employee named Muller, foreman of the girder shop at Mannheim-Rheinau, the parent plant. Despite many

A sample wooden girder which had survived in the attics of the Schutte-Lanz factory, left, compared with a drawing of a Cardington girder used in R.31 and R.32.   *Author and H. G. Parker*

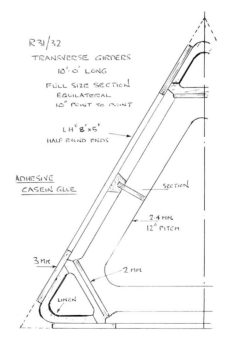

Revelations at the Schutte-Lanz works at Mannheim-Rheinau, with, left to right, Dr Ernst Langnickel, the author and Herr Strup.   *P. A. Bourne*

searching interviews conducted by the author, neither Claude Lipscomb nor his deputy Harold Parker nor any Cardington employee encountered had ever heard of or knowingly had met such an individual. On the other hand, these inquiries revealed that the layouts sent to Cardington from Smith Square all used metric dimensions, an almost unknown practice in engineering circles of the day, except when work was being carried out on projects from France.

Stephen Payne and H. May, the relevant Admiralty representatives at Cardington in those days, had both died by the time the author began his inquiries, but by good fortune access became available to notebooks left by Payne to his son Alan in Australia. From these it was discovered that Payne had indeed known the man Muller and had logged the fact that the British Ambassador in Switzerland had notified the Admiralty of his existence and his readiness to sell Schutte-Lanz secrets. Muller was eventually brought to England, where he was kept under police surveillance. An interpreter was provided by the Admiralty, although Stephen Payne claimed that he had been able himself to converse with him in German and believed him to be quite a practical sort of man "and a mine of information". He had also brought with him the new wonder glue, the cold water adhesive called "Kaltlein". This was the key to the manufacturing processes which produced ultra-lightweight girders made from plywood. From what has since been learned from other sources, Cardington's project was probably based on the designs of SL-7 and SL-8.

When the author visited the present-day Schutte-Lanz factory in Mannheim, the directors of the company made a search for information and discovered masses of files relating to the company's original airship activities, together with many previously unused photographs of Schutte-Lanz ships under construction. Even drawings of the SL-10, identical to the SL-11 shot down at Cuffley, were discovered. From the features of the SL-8 it was fairly evident that this had been the basis of most of the modified design that became the R.31. The overall length had been stretched to 615 feet and the gas capacity had risen from 1¼ million cubic feet in eighteen cells to 1½ million cubic feet in nineteen cells. The original four Maybach engines giving some 850 h.p. had been supplanted by six Rolls Royce Eagles giving nearly double that total power.

One valuable innovation was the direct attachment of the control car to a position well forward and flush to the hull, made possible by omitting the forward engine normally located there in Zeppelin designs. This feature, besides being superior aerodynamically, made life easier for the flight deck crew by the reduction in vibration, noise, and smells and by eliminating the need to climb an open ladder to get into the hull during flight.

In general terms, the primary structure looked reasonably orthodox but on closer examination the presence of Schutte-Lanz-type girder modules is indisputable. Sketches specially made for the author by Mr H. Parker reveal that these units were of spruce-stiffened three-ply, varnished and fireproofed, mostly 10 inch equilateral triangles about ten feet long. There were hardwood blocks in the extremity joints, reinforced with mild steel gusset plates. The complete girder was assembled only with cold water casein cement and sheathed in linen around the areas of stress. In situ, every girder was braced with diagonal wires and every ring with diametral and chordal wires, all of them solid piano wire, tensioned and sweated up on assembly without turnbuckles, mainly to save weight. Gas-cell retaining wires were spaced at about one foot pitch for the length of the ship, which became a complete birdcage of about 100 miles of piano wire.

The main triangular keel served as an internal corridor and was stressed to carry the loads of the water-ballast sacks, fuel tanks, bombs and the parachutes which were only then just coming into service. Initially, the six engines were arranged in three pairs of ply-skinned gondolas whose beautiful contours were ruined by enormous frontal radiators which, being fixed, could only have their cooling capacity varied by shuttering, unlike those in the Zeppelins which could be moved up or down, into or out of the slipstream. The two central engines were equipped for reversing.

When R.31 first flew in August, 1918, it was at once evident that Cardington had produced the biggest, fastest and most advanced airship constructed in Britain during the war. In only a little over two years from the opening of the station, the new union between Shorts and the Admiralty had evolved what was effectively a brand-new

In this view of the R.31 under construction the plywood girders and their intricate wire bracing are well seen. The triangular keel walkway also served to carry the heavier loads of fuel, ballast and bombs. Note also the gas-vent shaft and the partially inflated gas-cell.
H. G. Parker

ship, albeit with German assistance. Despite the limited experience both of Shorts and the R.C.N.C., the end results were undoubtedly enough to gladden the heart of Campbell and his superiors, who saw this as the first tangible step towards achieving their independence from Vickers. Because of his commitments in so many places, Campbell was not seen at Cardington a great deal but his influence was felt there in many ways. Now, with the actual arrival on the scene of the first real Admiralty rigid, the prospect of Cardington becoming the Royal Airship Works could not long be delayed.

The few who can still remember R.31 would agree that she was a beautiful creation and a real breakthrough. On her first flight under the command of Squadron Commander W. C. Hicks she flew around Bedfordshire for about two hours and was given a full speed run almost at once, registering a surprising maximum speed of 70 m.p.h. So impressive was this at the time that it was deemed to be more than was needed, and R.31 was modified by eliminating one of her six engine cars. This was achieved by placing one car aft on the centre line of the ship and removing the rear pair altogether. This had the pleasing result of diminishing the top speed by a mere 5 m.p.h. but enhancing the Useful Lift by about three tons; it also saved the weight of two crewmen and 150 pounds weight of fuel for each hour of flying.

Any big new ship, let alone a genuine prototype such as this, was bound to have teething troubles and even eccentricities. The rare phenomenon of R.31 was the behaviour of the wooden structure, which flexed to an extent sufficient for two men, posted at opposite ends of the keel, to lose sight of each other during turns. Stephen

The R.31 in her original six-engine configuration taking off on her first flight from Cardington in August, 1918, little more than a year after the opening of the station. The completion of the ship, built with predominantly local and inexperienced labour, in so short a time was a great achievement. *H. G. Parker*

Payne recorded a description of R.31's second flight on 16th October, 1918, when he flew with her as an Admiralty observer:

"I had climbed up to the top of the ship where we had a gun-platform. I remember feeling the absence of wind and noise, when suddenly a frightened face appeared at the top of the two-foot diameter tube with a rope ladder in it, and Hicks' First Lieutenant told me that the top of the vertical fin had collapsed—this explained why I felt that the nose of the ship was well up. Hicks had realised that the top vertical fin was acting as a kingpost supporting the two horizontal fins and it was the downward air passage on the horizontal fins that proved too much for the girder in the vertical fin. Hicks immediately dropped ballast to trim the ship by fifteen degrees at the bow. This enabled the air pressure at 40 knots to hold the horizontal fins in position, and so allowed the horizontal rudders to function. This accident happened near Cardington and many people saw crewmen on top of the airship tearing away great areas of fabric fouling the operation of the rudders and elevators. When the ship arrived back at the airfield and the engines were stopped, the horizontal fins naturally collapsed, due to the absence of air-pressure. All this was a

The port wing-car of the R.31, with a 300 h.p. Rolls Royce Eagle driving a two-bladed wooden propeller via a lever-operated clutch and reversing gear.
H. G. Parker

frightening experience for those on board, but we did not realise to the full what had happened. The ship's fin-girders were subsequently strengthened and while she had some minor troubles after this, there were none that were very serious."

In carrying out repairs the opportunity was taken to reduce the shape and size of the tail assembly, the dimensions having proved too great and the controls too powerful. One other modification made at this stage was the amputation of the tail cone and the siting of a gun-post with a wide arc of fire at that point, superior to that used on the Zeppelins.

R.31 was accepted into service without any more trials and set off on 6th November to fly to East Fortune, where she was to join R.29. She never reached her destination. Some girders had begun showing signs of failure, due possibly to her earlier flying with over-sensitive controls, and Squadron Commander Hicks aborted the flight half way and put in at Howden. The crew went on to Edinburgh by train,

The R.31 over Bedford on 16th October, 1918, after the upper dorsal fin had broken up. Amateur photographers were rare at that time, so this picture, taken from the roof of Hockliffe's bookshop, was a lucky find.   *Lilian Freshwater*

there to celebrate the end of the war five days later. As R.31 lay at Howden she occupied the berth earlier used by R.27, the ship that had been destroyed by fire in August. The fire-damaged roof had received only temporary repairs and consequently the R.31 suffered irreparable damage through wet storage during the ensuing winter. The ship was scrapped the following year.

By 11th November, 1918, Britain had completed and flown only eight rigid airships. Many others were fast approaching completion but were no longer required. At Cardington, construction continued slowly on R.32 and two others of metal construction and totally different design. To have reached this overall position from scratch in only a little over two years was a very commendable achievement.

CHAPTER SEVEN

A Bang or a Whimper?

THE GERMANS, recognising the effectiveness of the British Home Defence system, took steps to overcome the growing danger to their Zeppelins, giving immediate attention to existing airships on the one hand and considering major design improvements for new ships on the other.

Following the repatriation of one of the crewmen of L-33, Machinist's Mate Schultz, Strasser was shocked by the feedback of operational experience that this man was able to give. His technical and other criticisms learned from bitter experience caused alarm leading to immediate action. Restrictions were imposed on the weight of fuel carried, defensive weapons and ammunition were removed, and everything not considered essential, including anything in the nature of crew comforts, was eliminated.

Clearly, any such action was no more than a palliative and drastic design modifications were the highest priority. The first thing to go was the now outmoded rear gondola and its machinery, swiftly replaced, not only in new production but also retrospectively, with a new twin-engined car in which the engines were mounted in tandem and drove a single propeller. The assembly was considerably lighter and, being well streamlined, had far less drag. This was immediately followed by similar treatment of the main control car and the wing cars.

A much thinner metal strip was used for manufacturing the girders and fewer main rings were used, by spreading them out further, which in turn made another saving by reducing the number of gas cells for the same volume. The introduction of these many modifications, initially by degrees, caused little if any delay to the general delivery programme, a tribute to the efficiency of the factory planning engineers. LZ-95, the first Zeppelin to have virtually all the weight-saving changes, was the prototype of the new "U type", and the first to be known to the world as the "Heightclimber". Better known as L-48, she was launched on 22nd May, 1917, and commissioned the day after.

The improvement in performance was prodigious, Useful Lift reaching an unprecedented 85,800 pounds, 60 per cent of the total all-up weight; despite the removal of one engine, speed actually went up to 67 m.p.h. Simultaneously, as part of the programme to reduce vulnerability, at least the lower two thirds visible from below was painted black, the upper portion being left a light colour to minimise the effect of the sun's heat in expanding the gas.

At this period America entered the war; over the western front, the British and German air forces were locked in lethal combat and mutiny was a growing threat to the French. In the east, the Germans were leaning harder on the Russians, signs of the

Bolshevik revolution were beginning to show, and there came calls for more support from the Naval Zeppelins. In the south, General Thomsen, under Ludendorf, was beginning his planning for the running down of the Army Zeppelin Force, an event which finally came to pass at the end of July, 1917.

The tasks being imposed on Zeppelins by the Navy, however, were endless. On 16th June, 1917, L-48 set out with five other new ships on a raid on Britain to boost German morale. The usual faults prevented four of the six from reaching the coast, and Viktor Schutze, now deputy to Strasser, found his flagship L-48 accompanied only by L-42, commanded by Martin Dietrich. At about 2 a.m. L-42 was bombing Kentish seaports from an altitude of 15,000 feet, and after an amazing direct hit on a naval magazine at Ramsgate with a 660-pound bomb, turned back for Nordholz, reaching a height of 17,000 feet during the journey.

L-48 came inland at 2.10 a.m., flying at over 18,000 feet, and headed north-west for nine miles to Wickham Market. The airship cruised for eighty minutes over Suffolk and was tracked, accurately with location times, by police Specials and others, the forerunners of the Royal Observer Corps. When the author was researching in the Theberton area of Suffolk where L-48 crashed, one of the

Lost only three weeks after launching, the L-48 (LZ-95) was one of the first Zeppelins to be painted black as a defence against British attacks.

Kurt Puzicha

74

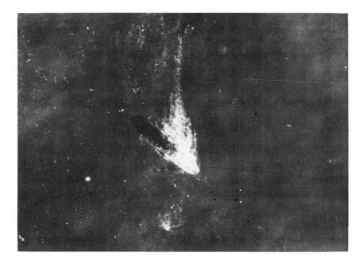

Looking down from an aeroplane on the blazing L-48 showering the sky with a fiery confetti of fabric. The original print of this previously unpublished photograph was given to Mrs R. Rowe by an R.F.C. officer on the day after the destruction of the L-48.

Mrs R. Rowe

documents produced by local people was a well illustrated brochure containing a narrative of the event by photographer J. S. Waddell, of nearby Leiston. Conventional histories normally only mention Second Lieutenant L. P. Watkins as responsible for shooting down L-48, but Waddell's account named two other pilots who were awarded decorations for their participation in the destruction of the airship. I eventually found one of them, Douglas Holder, who in 1969 was living at Danbury, near Chelmsford; he died on October 17th, 1978.

In the small hours of Sunday, June 17th, 1917, Holder and another pilot, Robert Saundby, later Air Marshal, took off from the experimental station at Orfordness in pursuit of the Zeppelin. Meanwhile, Watkins of No.37 Squadron in a Be12 from Goldhanger aerodrome on the Blackwater estuary, on a routine anti-Zeppelin patrol, had spotted the searchlights and gunfire and had headed in that direction.

Saundby in a single-seat D.H.2 and Holder in an Fe2b, with Sergeant Ashby as gunner, both climbed with throttles wide open in a desperate attempt to reach the "Heightclimber". As they continued their individual struggles to gain height and not lose sight of their quarry, none realised that L-48 had its own problems resulting mainly from high altitude; generally speaking, these were the effects of oxygen shortages and low air temperatures which made engines fail, turned the alcohol in the compass to ice, caused control cables to slacken and drop off their pulleys and crewmen to grow sluggish in the grip of anoxia, the stupor that comes as part of altitude sickness. With the compass out of action, two engines not functioning and the others giving only half power, L-48 radioed base for directional bearings and was advised to descend to 13,000 feet to find a tailwind and a less severe temperature.

In later years, the retired Squadron Leader Holder gave a graphic description of how he had observed the ship descending rapidly and unable to stop the fighter

75

aircraft closing in from several directions. He was insistent that had all the pilots combined to buzz the control car and merely fired warning lights and shots across the bows, they had a better than two-to-one chance of capturing her. Sixty years later, Douglas Holder was still very moved by the thought of the sailors who had died needlessly and so terribly when their airship might have been forced to land, probably at the nearby R.N.A.S. airship station at Pulham.

As the other pilots began firing, Holder found himself surrounded by machine-gun tracers, some coming through the hull of the ship from Watkins on the

Squadron Leader Douglas Holder, awarded the Military Cross for his attack on the L-48, seen at his Danbury home in 1972.   *Author*

other side and some from gunners on the ship. Very reluctantly, he gave Sergeant Ashby the order to fire, and in moments L-48 became a furnace in the sky, visible for over fifty miles and taking seven minutes or so to reach the ground.

There were three survivors of the crash, one of whom suffered a burst bladder and died seventeen months later, on the last day of the war. The other two, Mieth and Ellerkamm, survived until well after the Second World War. Despite the extensive destruction, the wreckage attracted the attention of Campbell's team who gleaned many new ideas for incorporation into later British rigids.

The Germans also had lessons to learn. They were apparent from the high altitude experiences of the crews of L-48 and her sister "Heightclimber". These were the days when pioneer crews discovered problems the hard way and technicians, under the pressure of war, provided answers to things like engines that first boiled and then froze solid, water-ballast that froze by the ton, and oxygen supplies that made crewmen ill.

The technical strategies of altitude options were dramatically indicated by two historic Zeppelin expeditions of opposite character in October, 1917. The summer of 1917 had passed with a few desultory sorties and aborted raids, but with settled weather in mid-October Strasser decided to use his growing fleet of "Heightclimbers" in the longer dark nights. On 19th October eleven ships, all of two million cubic feet capacity and in the serial range from L-41 to L-55, set off from four different stations. With the high Useful Lift values now available, Strasser was

The L-48 descended fairly slowly, taking about seven minutes to reach the ground at Theberton, Suffolk.
Douglas Holder

enabled to mount a mass raid at the extreme altitude needed to evade the defences; achieving that altitude required a division of available lift resulting in bomb loads of only two or three tons per ship, as against eighteen and even nineteen tons for ballast and five tons for petrol.

The squadron had been ordered to carry out a saturation raid on the industrial Midlands and North Country, arrive at various points in darkness and, as far as possible, maintain wireless silence. Ships' captains were quickly disorientated and became lost as powerful northerly winds built up and ships developed massive amounts of drift, while the navigators, unaccustomed to the new high altitudes, failed in most instances to make accurate spot identifications. The inevitable crop of engine failures, icing-up conditions, and crew casualties from frost-bite and altitude sickness all made their contributions to the catastrophe that began picking off those slowest to recognise the danger. Bombs were scattered haphazardly; one stick from L-53 fell to the south of Bedford, two miles from Cardington and only yards from John Bunyan's birthplace. The author still recalls the fearsome noise of the bombs as they fell, with a sound like that of a factory siren.

German reports of the whereabouts of the bombs dropped during the night bore

Above: The inquest into the deaths of the L-48 crew at Holly Tree Farm, Theberton, in June, 1917.
J. S. Waddell

Below: Lieutenant Victor Goddard and his engineers from Pulham salvaging wreckage from the L-48.
Sir Victor Goddard

The crew of the L-48. The three survivors were Leutnant-zur-See Otto Mieth, fourth from left in the front row, Machinist's Mate Wilhelm Uecker, standing behind him to the left, and Machinist's Mate Wilhelm Ellerkamm, fourth from right in the back row.   *Kurt Puzicha*

no resemblance to reality. Four of the eleven ships never returned, and the unhappy story of their misadventures would fill a book of its own. When dawn came the crews of L-44, L-45, L-49 and L-50 found they were scattered over France, where shortly they all came to grief, L-44 being shot down by French artillery and the others being forced to land by attacking French aircraft. L-49 remained intact after landing because the commander's signal pistol failed when he tried to fire the ship before being captured. Certain of the information derived from L-49 was later used by British designers and after the war drawings made of the ship formed the basis of the new American ship *Shenandoah*.

Simultaneously a second big operation was being planned in Bulgaria. This was for a technically daring long-range flight to a garrison under siege at Mahenge in German East Africa. The scheme had been devised as a pioneer airlift of critical supplies, and to make the attempt worthwhile an airship with an unprecedented lifting capacity was needed; the solution was to splice in a complete extra centre section of almost 100 feet which provided another half million cubic feet, just as Cardington would do to the R.101 thirteen years afterwards. The modified "V type" L-57 was now reclassified as a "W type", having an overall length of 743 feet, a volume of 2½ million cubic feet, a gross weight of 175,000 pounds and, most impressive of all, a Useful Lift of 114,700 pounds. It was originally intended that the Buttlar/Schiller team should undertake the flight, but the rather questionable honour was transferred to a less important crew under Ludwig Bockholt, since they were unlikely to return. As if to confirm his inexperience, Bockholt succeeded in wrecking L-57 by taking it out for a trial flight just before a storm broke; while he was attempting to rehouse the ship, the gale tore it away and hurled it around the countryside in a series of spectacular fires and explosions. Despite the loss, he was given another ship, L-59, similarly modified, but there were two more abortive attempts at depature before he was finally en route on 21st November, 1917.

L-59 carried the record weight of 15 tons true payload of emergency supplies for the besieged garrison, 20 tons of petrol for an extensive endurance flight and 10 tons of water-ballast, sufficient to provide control flexibility for a flight of medium altitude only. With this enormous overload, and a less than fully experienced captain and crew, L-59 performed what has since been regarded as one of the most successful flights ever to be made by an airship.

Bockholt flew from Bulgaria across the Mediterranean and up the Nile Valley almost to Abyssinia, at which stage he received a recall signal telling of the surrender of Mahenge. Turning about without landing, the dispirited crew continued flying through very high day-time and very low night-time temperatures which became very fatiguing. After a strenuous ninety-five hours they landed back at Jamboli, having flown 4,200 miles, with the 15-ton payload still intact. Unconsumed fuel would have kept them flying for another two and a half days.

Bockholt had proved his ability to drop a 15-ton bomb load on New York and to return to Germany without landing for refuelling.

The Naval Zeppelin Service continued its varied operations throughout the last year of the war and, although German aeroplanes now performed most of the bombing of Britain, it is noteworthy that Zeppelins in their occasional sorties were commonly flying at over 20,000 feet and in temperatures down to −30°F. British opposition continued unabated, and flying boats especially were having successes, while raids on Zeppelin bases also became profitable.

Virtually the finale came on 5th August, 1918, when Strasser set out to make a personal attack on Great Yarmouth using the month-old "X type" L-70 as his flagship, supported by four other big ships L-53, L-56, L-63 and L-65. L-70, commanded by Johann von Lossnitzer, was a magnificent ship, being the first to have seven engines and the first to exceed 80 m.p.h. She was also the first to carry 20 mm machine-cannon, and the overall combination undoubtedly promoted a level of confidence which events were about to destroy.

Droning along steadily over the North Sea in V-formation, the Zeppelins were detected by surface vessels and the defence services everywhere went on to standby alert hours before the raiders neared the coast. The news quickly spread about the town of Yarmouth, and gradually the whole sea front was thronged as residents and August holidaymakers sought vantage points. The Zeppelins held back, cruising slowly, reaching for height and waiting for darkness before attempting to overfly the coast. Just as the daylight was beginning to fade, the roar of engines on the South

Denes aerodrome at Yarmouth announced the take-off of thirteen de Havilland two-seater fighter-bombers, already deploying to make their interception of the invading Zeppelins.

Soon after dark, searchlights to the north of Yarmouth were seen weaving a pattern in and around low cloud and guns were firing at a Zeppelin skirting the coastline, probably L-56. Almost at the same time, at 10.20 p.m., some twenty miles out beyond Cromer, L-70 encountered a D.H.4 crewed by Egbert Cadbury and Bob Leckie, veterans of the Yarmouth station. The combatants met almost head-on at nearly 17,000 feet, and as they passed one another at a relative speed of about 140

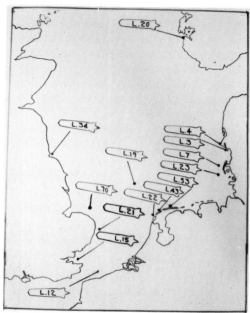

Zeppelins lost over the North Sea during the First World War.

m.p.h. gunner Leckie raked the great hull with the lethal Pomeroy ammunition; within seconds it was all over, and as the giant torch roared down into the sea, the driving force of the Naval Zeppelin Service went with it.

Within a week, L-53 fell to the ingenuity and bravery of the R.N.A.S., even though technically since 1st April they had been R.A.F. On 11th August, Rear Admiral Tyrwhitt's Harwich Force of cruisers and destroyers reached out into the German Bight. A part of the action was to try to entice out any of the remaining Zeppelins in daylight and destroy them with the latest invention. Eduard Prölss with L-53 fell for the trick as he cruised around suspiciously at 20,000 feet trying hard to observe the manoeuvres of Tyrwhitt's small fleet. What he failed to identify was a specially constructed lighter designed to be towed at high speed behind a destroyer. Lieutenant S. D. Culley climbed into the cockpit of the Sopwith Camel strapped down to a wooden platform built on the lighter. With throttle wide open, Culley roared off from the miniature platform pitching viciously in the turbulent wake of the destroyer and climbed steadily in search of his Zeppelin target. The climb took him nearly an hour, but once on a level with L-53, the last Zeppelin to be destroyed during the war, its fate was never in doubt.

Lieutenant Culley gradually descended to sea level and there ditched his Camel and waited patiently for his rescuers to arrive. After being retrieved, this now famous aeroplane was carefully refurbished and preserved. It is still a memorable sight as it sways gently under the roof of Lambeth's Imperial War Museum.

During the last few weeks of the war the Kiel Revolution, the mutiny of the lower ranks of the Navy, spread to the ground staff of several north German air stations, who virtually took over the bases as the belief spread that the Officer Class as well as the politicians had lost them the war. Early in 1919, with things still very chaotic, the Zeppelin aircrews and those mechanics still loyal were determined that no one should misuse their beloved Zeppelins. Their conspiracy of patriotism and defiance succeeded in destroying seven of the Zeppelins as they lay static and deflated in their sheds.

The constantly developed Maybach engine fitted to wartime Zeppelins. *Author*

CHAPTER EIGHT

Swords into Ploughshares

IN THE overall climate of a shattered civilisation, while the ministries of the involved nations struggled to re-establish a semblance of order, the bitterness of defeat still rankled deeply in some areas of Germany and it was by no means certain that the Armistice would be productive of a final peace settlement.

As a result of the rapid collapse of the German forces in the latter part of 1918, the British airship programme was overtaken by the event and only its momentum prevented an immediate cessation of work. Some of the work could conceivably be classed as experimental, but none of it as original development work, and the new airships under construction had little to commend them for any serious roles, either civil or military.

The period through to mid-1921 in Britain can be identified as a curious phase in which several different influences were emerging. The proponents of lighter-than-air craft campaigned constantly for the further development of airships for civilian transport. There was the odd situation in which the Admiralty, hitherto responsible for the sponsoring of production and also the manning of airships, now sought to shift the onus on to the Air Ministry. In April, 1918, men of the airship crews, by definition sailors, had become aircraftmen of the newly formed Royal Air Force. Crews were bewildered by selective demobilisation and the uncertainty of a civilian future. Many chose to stay in the highly specialised airship world which they knew, understood and, in most instances, thoroughly enjoyed. The question no-one could possibly answer was, how long would it last?

At the end of 1918 there were six British rigids in existence, Numbers 23, 24, and 25 and R.26, R.29, and R.31. Britain's first flyable rigid No.9 was scrapped in the summer of 1918 and the R.31 was lying at Howden in a dubious condition, destined never to fly again. The serviceability of the remaining ships was questionable, the very short life of the gas-cells and envelope often becoming the determining factor. None of the ships survived to the end of 1919, most being scrapped on site.

Of the ships laid down during the war, many were immediately deleted, but those allowed to proceed were the now legendary "33 class". Originally eleven ships of this new class had been ordered during the war, but only the first two, R.33 and R.34, resembled their German counterpart, albeit with a few minor modifications. R.33, built at Armstrong-Whitworth, and R.34, at Beardmore, came into service in March, 1919, and were the two most successful and most historic airships ever produced in Britain.

The R.33, undoubtedly a rarity and a much-loved ship, with 800 hours flying time and a further 300 experimental hours at the mooring mast, gave a greater service and lasted longer than any other ship Britain ever produced. During the nine years of her life she survived many adventures and an almost unending series of experiments, including the launching and retrieving of fighter aircraft in flight, some of which the author witnessed at Cardington.

Her log books show that she was launched at Selby on 6th March, 1919, and flew for three hours, then there is an unrecorded gap until 18th June. From that time on, the evidence is graphic and shows that her flying life was in three phases. During the first of these, covering the period from 18th June, 1919, to 14th October, 1920, she made 23 separate flights, totalling 337 hours. Flight Lieutenant G. M. Thomas was in command during this period.

On 2nd July, 1919, as R.34 took off from East Fortune to fly the Atlantic, R.33 left Pulham at the start of one of the strangest airship flights, cruising over London trailing banners exhorting Londoners to buy Victory Bonds. The possibility that some people might be too busy to notice this airborne spectacular was taken care of by the brass band that was playing full blast on the open gun platform on top of the hull.

Taken at Pulham in 1921, this photograph shows men who were to become the best known of British airship captains. Left to right are Flight Lieutenant R. S. Montague, who died in the R.38 crash; Flight Lieutenant A. C. Irwin, later commander of R.101; Flight Lieutenant H. V. Drew, last commander of R.34; Flight Lieutenant G. M. Thomas, who died as first officer of R.38; Commander Louis Maxfield, U.S.N., commander designate of R.38; Flight Lieutenant A. H. Wann, commander of R.38 and a survivor of the crash, though severely injured; and Flight Lieutenant H. Scroggs, engineer officer of R.36. Sitting in front are Flight Lieutenant T. Elmhirst, navigator and later to become Air Marshal Sir Thomas Elmhirst; and Flight Lieutenant F. Butcher, a navigator in training.   *Lord Ventry*

The Top Brass in the airship world—a band playing on top of the R.33. This picture rewarded the author for his ten-year search for evidence supporting a rumour that a band had actually played on the airship.

Ted Stupple

In the autumn of 1920 a winter overhaul was required, but space at Pulham was now at a premium since the arrival of the two surrendered Zeppelins, L-64 and L-71. R.33 therefore flew to Howden on 14th October and did not return until 2nd February, 1921.

Then began the second phase of her varied and useful career and another sixty-two flights were made in the six months ending on 18th August, 1921, logging another 290 flying hours in the process. The first two months were devoted almost entirely to crew training in the techniques of what the log book calls "landing to the mast". On 17th March during flight trials over Essex she circled for an hour over Tilbury while engineers and riggers rectified a jammed rudder. During April she was performing the first of several night flights connected with the checking of the new Croydon airport lighting facilities.

On several occasions, R.33 anticipated modern helicopter practices by serving as an observation platform to monitor traffic congestion at Epsom and Ascot. In July, 1921, a timber-built mooring mast was erected at Croydon, but it was used only twice when R.33 moored to it on the nights of 14th and 15th July. It is believed that air traffic control and the pilots of foreign aircraft took objection to these exercises and the mast was therefore removed.

On 30th July, 1921, she carried out full power trials and established a maximum speed of 52 knots, about 5 knots slower than her German predecessor. On 18th August she flew from Pulham to Cardington in 1 hour 47 minutes and there she lay in a care and maintenance condition for another four years. Not until the next and last British airship programme would the shape of R.33 again be seen over our countryside. Till then, she lay in the berth so recently vacated by the disaster-smitten R.38 and next to the abandoned and unfinished R.37. Concerning the immediate post-war months, Lieutenant-Commander Cole had this to say:

"On 11th November, 1918, the Armistice was declared and on 12th November, Sutcliffe and I sent in a written application to return to the Naval Constructors Department in such terms that Campbell could not refuse, so that he was left with May only. Nevertheless, on 18th November I was instructed to go to Germany together with an Air Force officer and an Intelligence Officer from the War Office. This arose because the Germans refused to allow officers from the British Fleet which went to Kiel to enforce the terms of the Armistice to enter Germany to deal with the Zeppelins. A telegram was sent to Marshal Foch asking him to arrange for an overland mission and I was chosen to be in charge. I remember meeting Dr Eckener and also Countess Zeppelin (If looks could kill, I should not be alive today writing this letter!)."

Cole followed this with an extraordinary account of how the three officers made their way in haste to France without identity papers or written authority and with

The R.34, first aircraft ever to cross the Atlantic both ways. The escutcheon on the bows now belongs to the Cardington Museum and is on loan to East Fortune, from where the R.34 began her transatlantic flight. *George Swain*

very little cash. After commandeering three aeroplanes with pilots they flew to Berlin and there moved out to the various Zeppelin bases, deflating the Zeppelins and otherwise immobilising them.

Only two months after Cole had communicated this information to me, I found myself in Germany with Dr Eckener's one-time right-hand man Hans von Schiller, who well remembered meeting Cole in those very bleak days. There was no doubting

Lieutenant-Commander A. P. Cole, of the Royal Corps of Naval Constructors.
Mrs M. A. Cole

his sincerity and pleasure in learning that Cole was still (in 1973) among the survivors of that age.

Schiller told me how the western powers had been determined to block all further Zeppelin developments, ostensibly because they posed a military threat but in reality because they feared Germany might win the peace with a global airline service operated with Zeppelins. He mentioned in particular that Germany still had the last two Naval Zeppelins intact, L-71 and L-72, of 2½ million cubic feet, and that it had leaked out that he and Ernst Lehmann had been planning to fly them both to America; Schiller with L-71 would press on non-stop across America as far as its Pacific seaboard, Lehmann with L-72 would cross the Atlantic to New York and there do an about turn and, also without landing, fly directly back to Germany. At a time when nobody of any nationality had made even a one-way crossing of the Atlantic by air such possibilities were as dramatic and improbable as a flight to the moon.

When the British government discovered what was afoot, action was taken immediately at the highest levels to prevent it taking place. Ultimately the Atlantic crossing by airship was made for the first time by a British-built airship, the R.34, with a British crew, barely two weeks after the first non-stop aerial crossing had been made by the British pilots Alcock and Brown in their Vickers Vimy aeroplane. The

R.34 set off on 2nd July, 1919, the nineteenth anniversary of the very first Zeppelin flight. It is doubtful whether this was significant to the crewmen at the time, since they themselves were probably rather more disappointed they had not been able to get away sooner and beat the aeroplane as the first across.

Most people are aware of the R.34's effort, which has commonly been accepted as a magnificent achievement; never does one hear it acknowledged that it was nearly a disaster and that it might have been better if it had never been attempted, at least with a ship of such inadequate design. In taking 108 hours for the outward journey, the margin between success and catastrophe was a matter of less than two hours' reserve of fuel. Units of the U.S. Navy actually put to sea, half expecting to have to take the R.34 in tow or, if it came to the worst, to mount a search for possible survivors. An eleventh-hour decision changed the agreed landing place from Mineola to Montauk in an attempt to shorten the journey. Accordingly the ground-handling party rushed off to the short-fall landing ground, arriving there just in time to see R.34 press on to its originally named destination. As Major Pritchard parachuted down to give instructions to a hurriedly gathered ground crew, and thus became the first man ever to arrive in America by air, General Maitland recorded in his diary the indisputable fact "Our luck is in after all. What a relief!"

This was only one of several British airship flights which hindsight has shown ought never to have been made.

Coming so soon after a war of daily death and destruction, such risks may well have appeared to be of a trivial character. Perhaps it was better that way. Two men who would probably agree with that view are the two surviving members of the R.34 crew, Fred Browdie and Billy Ballantyne, the latter ironically being the one man who should never have been aboard and became the first stowaway in air history.

Both men were experienced members of R.34's regular crew, having served during the war on non-rigids and most of the rigids from No.9 onwards. Unfortunately for Ballantyne, however, when the final crew list for the Atlantic journey was being prepared it was realised that loading limits would restrict the numbers carried. A.C.2 W.W. Ballantyne, born 29th April, 1898, at Newcastle, was the one name that did not appear in any of the crew rosters and this was completely unacceptable to him; Billy Ballantyne was going to be on that flight if it cost him everything.

At 1.23 a.m. on 2nd July, 1919, at East Fortune aerodrome near Edinburgh, a bugle was blown and a ground handling party began walking R.34 out of her shed stern first, loaded, with her crew already at their posts. Her gas-cells were 99 per cent full and she was carrying three tons of water ballast, one ton of lubricating oil, one ton of drinking water, various engine spares, 545 pounds of assorted foodstuffs and about 160 pounds of Billy Ballantyne, hidden away high on a girder between the gas-cells.

As the 700 members of the handling party held the over-buoyant ship steady, thousands of gallons of petrol were steadily gushing into the cylindrical tanks lining both sides of the catwalk, until eventually it was possible to verify that the ship was in equilibrium with nearly 16 tons of fuel aboard; another 20 gallons might have been loaded, enough to keep the ship cruising for the same number of minutes, had it not been for the stowaway. Hanging on tight to his perch in the darkness like some bat in a belfry, Ballantyne prayed.

General Maitland logged the fact that at 1.42 a.m. Major Scott gave a hand signal to the bugler who sounded the call that heralded the start of the flight and caused 700 pairs of hands to release the ship, which rose up and disappeared instantly into cloud, while the crew could still hear the cheering as they slowly flew away. Twelve hours later a pale and much weakened Ballantyne succumbed to the effects of cold, cramp,

Squadron Leader William Ballantyne, the first stowaway in aeronautical history, seen here in Canada during the Second World War.
William Ballantyne

hunger and violent sickness incurred from inhaling the free hydrogen escaping from the gas-trunks during the flight. Sick and dejected, he crawled down as far as the keel, where in a short time he was discovered by others of the crew and taken before Major Scott in the control-car. After the shock and the reprimands were over, Major Scott made it abundantly clear that it was very lucky for Ballantyne that they were now over the Atlantic or he would have been dumped over the side with a parachute and left to walk home by himself.

Though Ballantyne was officially in disgrace, it says much for the perspicacity of General Maitland that Ballantyne was among the crew of the new R.80 in the following year. In the fullness of time, Ballantyne not only progressed to a Sergeant Pilot, no mean feat during the 1920's, but ultimately received a commission and was instructing overseas during the Second World War.

After its return to Pulham from the American trip, R.34 came to Cardington for

The rear engine-car of the R.34. Technical features to be seen are: (a) Extended top radiators. (b) Ladder into hull. (c) Engine air intake. (d) Emergency helm. (e) Flame trap exhaust. (f) Oil cooler. (g) Landing shock absorber.   *William Ballantyne*

a major refit and to have its nose modified for mooring attachments, which latter items not being immediately available were never fitted. From Cardington, R.34 moved to the Yorkshire operational base of Howden, for general training purposes. Performing this role on 27th January, 1921, she set off from Howden with a class of R.A.F. trainees on board who succeeded in getting themselves lost. Had the final outcome of this flight not proved so costly, the story might have made hilarious reading for its succession of human errors.

Just as the ship was getting airborne, Hitchcock, the wireless operator, realised that he had omitted to check out the correct signal code to be used for this flight. With his Aldis signalling lamp he called Flying Control and asked for the required information. This obtained, he sat back to watch the preparations being made for one of the crew members to make a parachute descent. The time was 12.20, and as the ship climbed away the riggers patrolled among the gas-cells, checking expansion during the ascent and looking for malfunctioning gas-valves. At 12.35 the parachutist made his exit and Hitchcock was able to lower his aerials in order to start W/T transmissions and began tuning his equipment. Every attempt to contact base proved abortive and only then, when he used the wavemeter to check his calibrations, did he discover the instrument to be unserviceable; he had forgotten to check it out when he collected it from the W/T stores before boarding the ship. For the rest of the afternoon he continued his efforts to make contact with Howden, but without success. It was several hours before either he or the operator at base realised that the wrong code had been given to Hitchcock in the hurry of his departure. It was dark, with the R.34 well out to sea, before the operator at Howden decided it was time for the C.O. to be told of the situation.

The moment General Maitland was told he ordered a recall of R.34 as soon as a contact could be established. This was not achieved until as late as 19.34, by which time the ship was well away from base and the weather was deteriorating.

At this point the following letter, written by one of the crew to another airshipman, Mr Sidney Duke, describes events with realism.

Dear Old Sid,   2nd Feb, 1921
Your unexpected letter to hand this morning. Many thanks for it Sid. Well now for the story. In a panic of a hurry we left Howden at 12 noon on Thursday. On board were thirteen navigators and our own three officers with Captain Drew in command. In all, the crew numbered forty-one. We had on board 2,203 gallons of petrol and 6 tons of water. Also rations for 18 hours. The return was intended for 7 a.m. Friday morning, but as you will see, the luck turned against us everyway.
Those "Navigator" crowd started by losing us. We flew at 1,000 feet height but were flying 1,100 so no blame is attached to the elevator man. At midnight, the watches changed over and while I was having cocoa in the crew space, at 12.10 we struck violently at a speed of 43 knots.
The whole ship quivered like a whiplash and in the darkness that followed, all was more or less confusion. I made for the wing-car exit myself. The keel lights were intact but the fore-car was properly upset and girders were buckled in all sorts of shapes. The Douglas casings broke and the forward propeller was smashed completely, also the struts. In the engine-room was a regular flower bed of heather, furze, etc. Strange to say, the controls were unhurt and we carried on steering with the aid of a hand-lamp. So much for the forward car. The wing-cars escaped. The after car propeller also went smash. Then we were left with two engines to battle against an increasing wind of 18 m.p.h. at 1,000 feet. As you can guess Sid, we were unable to estimate what the damage was until daybreak and what I have described before is what we found. Our aerial was carried away and we managed on a flying strand of copper wire found in the keel somewhere. Not so bad Sid?

Clearly, an attempt was being made during the night to return inland and serious errors of navigation occurred, so that the ship came to overfly high ground without the crew being aware of it until the impact with the top of a hill, somewhere on the Yorkshire Moors. At that point, it was very much a case of Up ship and away and back to sea before anything worse could happen; in fact it would have been better if they had decided to stay out at sea all night in the first place.

To return to the crewman's account:

After nine hours we reached the coast, which by the way we could see right from daybreak. We proceeded up the Humber as far as Goole and then turned inland. The wind was all the time increasing. We were travelling crab fashion all the time. Do you know Sid, it was H--- steering. I never steered a ship like it in all my life and I've steered a few times! Fifteen degrees either side even for two hours takes some doing.

With the breakages of propellers, three of the five engines were rendered useless. It is a fact that the last twenty miles to Howden took three hours. The remaining two engines were being run at full throttle to make any headway at all; they were not of a type renowned for reliability and had either one failed, the ship must have drifted out to sea and been wrecked.

> Well Sid, we reached Howden at about 5 p.m. Friday evening. We came down from 600 feet to 300 and found the altimeter only 200 feet out. Then the fun began. Drew made a posh landing. He overshot the landing party and drifted back and down at the same time. As they got hold of us, we smashed into the earth, smashing the forward car completely; most marvellous thing of all, all wire suspensions held. Everyone stuck to the ship to the last. The control car was smashed up into the keel and so was the after car. After some ten of these bumps, "Abandon Ship" was given and the escapes were truly marvellous. I got off with burned fingers. The ship was moored in an hour and the bows were torn completely off and she sank down in the glare of the searchlights like a dying leviathan of long ago. Do you know Sid, it nearly made me cry to hear her wrench herself asunder. Two years Sid, and then to tear herself to pieces before our very eyes. All the crew were heartbroken to see her go. And now nothing.

When R.34 did reach base, the ground crew tried getting her back into her shed but turbulence, caused by the wind curling over the roof, grabbed the ship as though it were a toy. First it was bounced hard up and down, then the tail went up by seventy feet, with the ground crew still courageously hanging on to the rear

The wreck of the R.34 at Howden on 28th January, 1921. Serious damage was caused to the control car when it was crushed into the hull, miraculously without causing an outbreak of fire.   *Gerry Long*

The first British airship to carry a civil registration, the R.36, is seen here at the Pulham mast. The photograph clearly shows the passenger saloon and the engine-cars removed from the surrendered L-71.

George Swain

gondola's handling rails. With the damage increasing by the second, the very real danger was that escaping hydrogen would be ignited by a spark. The attempt to berth her in the shed had to be abandoned and she was staked down in the open where, on the following day, axes completed the demolition. The end of the R.34 was as ignominious as it was unmerited.

It was decided to convert the three other ships of the "33 Class", ordered but not completed as such, into the "Heightclimber" formula, but even this idea failed to mature. One, R.35 at Armstrong-Whitworth, was cancelled just before the completion of the R.33 prototype in the same factory. Another, R.37, was allowed to proceed at a reduced rate at Cardington, alongside R.38. By the time Cardington closed down in August, 1921, R.37 was 95 per cent completed. When the works reopened in 1924 to start on the R.101, the R.37 was scrapped to make room and R.33, then in the same hangar, was given a new lease of life.

The only one of the three to fly was R.36 at Beardmore's, and she did so only because of a further experiment made in the attempt to keep the airship concept alive at a very difficult time. R.36 retained its added volume, brought in by the stretch modification, but the engine-car which was normally an appendage to the control-car in these types was neatly removed and its place taken by the forward end of a passenger saloon. This extended some 130 feet rearwards and was designed to accommodate fifty passengers, who were provided with a small lounge and sleeping facilities of a sort, as well as toilets and a small galley.

Launched on 1st April, 1921, she bore the first civil registration, G-FAAF, to be seen on a British rigid. She performed her maiden flight of 20 hours on the way to

The damaged R.36 stowed away in the shelter of the Pulham hangar at the expense of the hurriedly demolished Zeppelin L-64.   *Albert Hunt*

Pulham and was out again two days later, when she thoroughly scared the Air Ministry officials on board by diving more than 2,000 feet as a result of the collapse of both the upper and starboard stabiliser fins. This frightening experience did little to enhance the image of airship travel for those who were sampling it for the first time. Passengers also complained that the positioning of the engine-cars made their quarters very noisy. From a technical standpoint, the machinery installations were most interesting. In place of the Sunbeam Maori engines used in R.33 and R.34 and which gave about 250 h.p. each, the bigger Sunbeam Cossack of 350 h.p. was employed in R.36. Three such engines were placed in individual cars at the positions typical of the "33 Class" ships, and in addition two extra gondolas were placed well forward on either side; these were the complete Maybach engine-cars removed from the surrendered L-71 at Pulham.

After a few more publicity flights, R.36 was pensioned off and stored at Pulham, but not before suffering damage when she apparently tried to knock the mooring mast over. One of the surrendered German airships, L-64, was taken out and dismantled to make space for R.36 in what was to be her final resting place.

By now the pattern of British rigid airship philosophy was evident.

A. P. Cole had said only one man in this country, Barnes Wallis, could have equalled Dr Eckener in ingenuity. What was it that earned for Wallis the accolade from one of the senior members of "the opposition", and what exactly was Wallis doing during this period? To appreciate the remarkable skills of Barnes Wallis it is necessary to return to the earlier No.9 and No.23 types, when he was learning his trade under Pratt and it was evident that they had inherited a design legacy from the early Vickers experience with the *Mayfly*. Until No.9 flew in the autumn of 1916, they had no first-hand experience on which to judge the merits or vices of the work they had performed. With the restrictions imposed on them by the small size of the Barrow shed, both Pratt and Wallis were hopelessly tied and completely frustrated.

The fact that the much larger assembly hall and back-up manufacturing plant never matured was not a case of broken promises but was due to the inability of civil engineers to solve constructional problems in time. Wallis eventually found himself in charge, fired with the ambition to design and produce a technically efficient airship which owed little or nothing to anyone else's ideas. Most important of all, it owed nothing to Admiralty ideas. Time to completion, however, bore no relationship to the actual working time involved. Sanction for the project had been obtained as early as November, 1917, but it was not until March, 1918, when R.26 left the cradles, that space was available for erection. Within months the war ended and a brake was placed on virtually all airship work. Consequently, it was not until July, 1920, that the fruits of his work became evident.

The vital statistics of his new R.80 underline the handicap imposed by the size of its birthplace. With an overall length of 535 feet and a maximum diameter of 70 feet, the R.80 had a 1¼ million cubic feet hull containing fifteen gas-cells. The most striking feature was the attention paid to streamlining. The machinery comprised four Maybach engines, totalling 900 h.p., driving three pusher propellers. Single-engined wing cars were disposed on both sides of the hull, while the control-car forward carried the other two engines geared to a single propeller. With this arrangement, not only did the location of wing cars impart an ability to circle in tight turns and facilitate other intricate manoeuvres, but in cruising flight it was very convenient to rest either the pair of forward engines or the two wing engines and cruise economically at half power.

The new vessel quickly found favour with those who flew it, but inevitably, due to its small size, it had no greater value than to serve as a training ship and to develop engineering principles for use later. Since its performance capabilities in both speed and Useful Lift were almost identical to the German "Q type" Zeppelins of the same volume, the inference is that Wallis had now proved his ability to build as good an

The first flight of the R.80, Barnes Wallis's first completely original design, at Barrow on 19th July, 1920. This airship proved efficient but was not effectively utilised except as a training ship for the American crew for the ill-fated R.38.   *William Ballantyne*

airship as the Germans. Most of her Service flying time of 73 hours was performed during the spring and summer of 1921 when training was given to the American aircrew waiting to take over the R.38, then being constructed for them at Cardington. R.80 finished up being stored at Pulham in the following September and lay there with the other ships until demolished in 1925 with the start of a new programme.

Long before all this had happened, other events had begun influencing the situation at Cardington during the last year of the war. Opinions varied in Whitehall in early 1918 as to the expected duration of the war, but the basic war policy could only dictate a continuation of war effort to match possible continued resistance by the Germans. In accord with this, the Admiralty saw fit to maintain and expand its connection with rigid airships, in spite of the amalgamation of the air arms of the Royal Navy and the Army on 1st April which produced a whole new set of administration problems.

Although such a change could affect the possible role of the airship in wartime, the Admiralty sponsored a new and powerful airship weapon as an adjunct to the Fleet. A committee considered the tactical requirements to be met by the new type of ship and, in general terms, it was demanded that all the existing criteria of speed and altitude and endurance known to have been achieved by German technology were to

96

be exceeded and combined within a single type of ship for which the design group assembled by Campbell was to be fully responsible.

What this meant to Campbell was that he would be aiming at a design that resembled the German "Heightclimber" both in size and appearance, and also in making use of the lightest possible structures. In practical terms, it immediately reduced the problem to one of designing the biggest possible ship that could be constructed within the overall length of 700 feet of all the sheds except those of Vickers. For the first and only time the design was completely an Admiralty one, and it was thus that the concept of the R.38 was first born at 10 Smith Square in August, 1918.

The interpretation of this highly exacting specification became a joint effort between Campbell and his team of naval architects on the one side and Lipscomb and his men from Shorts on the other. Campbell's people were responsible for the structural guide drawings, for the profile chosen and for the selection of engines, armament and ancillary equipment. Shorts carried out the detail design work and the manufacture, both aspects being under the scrutiny of resident Admiralty overseers.

Three ships of the type were ordered but, with the end of the the war coming sooner than expected, only the Cardington R.38 was permitted to proceed.

Seen here in front of the Cardington design office in 1921 are the majority of those responsible for the creation of the R.38.   *H. G. Parker*

A quick look at the way the design formula took shape reveals that 699 feet of the internal shed length of 700 feet was taken up by the overall length of the R.38, and by siting all the gondolas so as to get the benefit of height within the shed a maximum diameter of 85½ feet was achieved. These major dimensions resulted in a displacement of 2¾ million cubic feet, which at the time made it the largest airship ever constructed anywhere in the world. While the required lift was being sought by sheer volumetric size, many other devices were tried in pursuit of the same aim. Despite the conventional practice of using eighteen to twenty separate gas-cells, R.38 used only fourteen. Girderwork was manufactured to such a light pattern that the designers even had to impose restrictions on crew movements and limits on the number permitted at any given position on board. Later, in a written report, the ship's commander told how he had to have duckboards laid on the gangway in the keel because it was so weak. While all these measures achieved the required altitude, high speed could only be attained with high power. Initially it was thought that the Maori engines used on many other British ships would suffice, but eventually the bigger Cossacks, as used on R.36, were chosen. Totalling 2,100 h.p., six Cossacks in six gondolas were slung well spread out along both sides of the hull to equalise the loads on the structure.

In 1919, when the economy measures began to bite, the opportunity was taken of selling the R.38 to America. The United States Navy had no rigids and was anxious to create a force of such vessels to extend its flying experience, hitherto restricted to non-rigids. In October, 1919, contracts were exchanged, R.38 was reprieved and work went ahead, increasingly supervised now by the Air Ministry who were in the process of inheriting these complex responsibilities. Among these responsibilities was the training of the American crew who would have to ferry the R.38 back to Lakehurst, New Jersey. For this, the R.32 and later the R.80 were used. As the work on R.38 progressed, the Americans went to Cardington to study the specialised work being carried out there, a new experience for most of them. Living locally, they spent many months acquiring alternately engineering knowledge at Cardington and flight handling experience at Howden and Pulham.

On 23rd June, 1921 R.38 ascended from Cardington for the first time and on 26th June the officer in charge of flight trials, Major J. E. M. Prichard, reported that "owing to the trouble experienced with the rudder and elevator controls, it was impracticable to fly at more than 40 knots, and in consequence the information obtained from the flight was meagre. As speed was increased, the slack side of the rudder and elevator controls (cables) eased up to such an extent that they wrapped round the taut side and . . . caused the controls to jam. Owing to the increasing slackness of the slack side of the controls with increase of speed, the chains in the control-car at times jumped their sprockets and both rudders and elevators got out of step. The trouble was thought to be partially due to the new type of planes being

At the time of its construction the R.38 was the biggest airship to have been built. Its size is apparent from this picture showing its 699 ft. length barely contained within the 700 ft. internal length of the Cardington shed.　　　　*U.S. Navy archives*

over-balanced . . . The engines ran with a considerable amount of irregularity and require careful adjustment before the ship is again taken into the air."

Major Pritchard had taken an important part in the flight of R.34 to America. His report on R.38's first flight was confirmed by Flight Lieutenant A. H. Wann as Captain, and the latter's report reveals also that the flight did not take place until late in the day, preparations being made during the day on the strength of the weather forecasts.

> "At 21.00 the temperature and the wind had abated sufficiently to enable the ship to be handled out of the shed with a reasonable degree of safety and at 21.52 the ship left the ground without incident. The ship was taken at a slow speed to pressure height (2,300 feet) and then to 2,500 to ensure that the automatic valves were working properly. Height was lowered to 1,800 feet and the speed increased to between 35 and 40 knots. At this speed however, considerable trouble commenced to occur with the controls. The coxswains found the controls extremely difficult to work . . . thus putting the rudders and elevators out of place with each other. A landing was effected at daybreak and the ship returned to her shed at 05.00.
>
> "A conference having been held to determine what was wrong with the controls it was decided to cut a certain amount off the leading edge of the top rudder. This work was completed at 18.00 on 27th June . . . and the ship was taken out for her second trial at 21.45 . . . exhaustive data was obtained under varying circumstances but it was not deemed advisable to increase the speed beyond 48 knots . . . the ship returning to her shed at 04.30.
>
> ". . . it was determined that the movable parts were over-balanced and therefore a decision to remove a certain portion off all the movable planes was arrived at . . . and this entails laying the ship up for a fortnight."

Already the political pressures were building up due to the Ministry's anxiety to finish with the airship programme, and the U.S. Navy Department was getting impatient and wanted to receive the airship as rapidly as possible. When R.38 left Cardington to fly to Howden on 17th July, 1921, it had been tested only twice, and then quite inadequately. As it disappeared over the northerly horizon, Lipscomb and his men began packing their bags, wondering what the future might hold for them at the parent company's base in Rochester.

If ever a ship was doomed from the start it was R.38. On her delivery flight to Howden she went into a steep dive, and only by the intervention of one of the deck officers did she survive. On arrival at her new trials base, an examination revealed a breakage of girders sufficient to require major repairs, and in the opinion of Pritchard to warrant a full investigation into the design of R.38, now bearing the new American designation of ZR-2. On 11th August, 1921, Prichard submitted a lengthy evaluation of the trials up to that date:

> "The problem of getting this ship ready for the trans-Atlantic flight is one of considerable difficulty. The Americans wish to leave at latest by the end of August, owing to the increasingly bad weather in the Atlantic and on the American coast which is likely to be encountered after the end of August. On the other hand, R.38 is a ship of extremely light construction and is comparable with certain classes of destroyer and battle cruisers which cannot steam at full speed into a heavy sea. R.38 was designed for super-efficient war

Technical superintendent Commander J. Dyer, U.S.N., third from left, with Admiralty overseer Stephen Payne, fourth from left, and members of the American naval crew for the R.38 at Cardington during the later stages of construction. *U.S. Navy archives*

work in the North Sea where, owing to enemy action, it was essential that an extremely high performance should be provided. This was achieved in three ways: by improving the economical use of materials; by increasing the size of the ship; and by cutting down factors of safety.

"With a new ship of this sort it is therefore essential that it should be thoroughly tried out to ensure that it possesses the necessary degree of staunchness before setting out on a long flight. The position is at present that the ship has not been put up to full speed and has never been flown in disturbed air conditions and therefore, from the airworthiness and staunchness point of view, the trials so far carried out are of little value. It is necessary that before the ship flies to America she should first be proved to be airworthy by British personnel and then handed over to the Americans who will then carry out one or two flights in her to accustom themselves to her general behaviour. The ship will then be ready for her trans-Atlantic flight.

"Owing to the unsettled weather conditions and to the lack of mooring-mast facilities, it is extremely doubtful if the necessary flying can be got in between the present date and September 1st. Secondly, having proved out the ship as airworthy and handed over to the American personnel for their one or two flights to accustom themselves to her handling, it may in addition be necessary to wait for some time for favourable weather in the Atlantic."

Twelve days after Pritchard had issued that report, the latest of several which had clearly revealed the areas of danger into which they were heading, R.38 went off on what was to be her last flight. Pritchard, now using his R.A.F. title of Flight Lieutenant, was accompanied by Maitland, now Air Commodore. After some relatively mild working up trials, R.38 sat out for the night, gently cruising up and down the coast until dawn. A variety of basic tests were flown during the day, including a number of speed trials in which the engines were progressively opened up until a speed of 62 knots was obtained. During the late afternoon, the weather was calm with a general overcast of low cloud and the wind no more than a light breeze, with the barometer at 1018 and falling very gradually. Many hundreds of factory workers scurrying home for their evening meals at half past five were attracted by the roar of multiple engines overhead as the huge bulk of the R.38/ZR-2 broke cloud over Hull and was seen travelling rapidly in a south-westerly direction. Its height was variously estimated by witnesses as being between 1,500 and 2,500 feet and its speed as about 60 m.p.h.

All who saw it as it cleared the city and began passing over the River Humber were unanimous in their accounts of seeing it changing direction repeatedly and rapidly. Then great wrinkles and folds were seen, showing up as vertical lines about two-thirds of the way back along the hull.

The interior of the control car of the R.38, with the rudder helm at the front and the elevator helm and engine-room telegraphs for the six engines in their customary positions. *H. G. Parker*

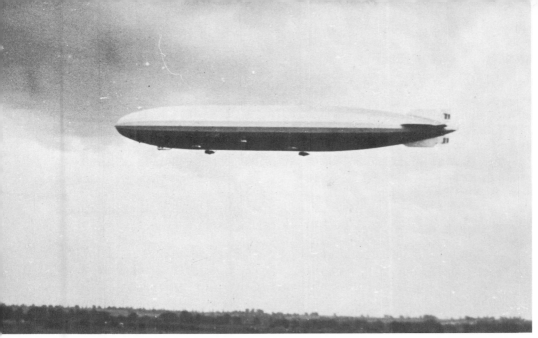

Above: The R.38 leaves Cardington for Howden on 17th July, 1921.

Blake and Edgar

Below: At Howden R.38 receives its American service number ZR-2.

U.S. Navy archives

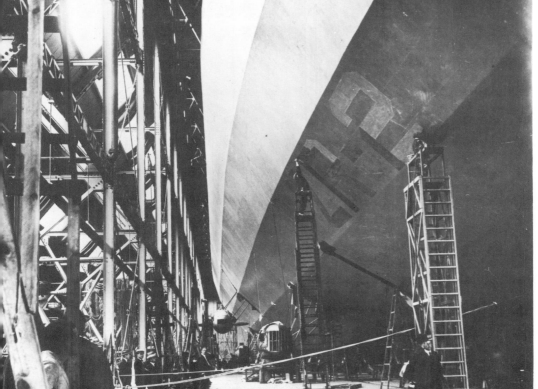

As the crowds on the ground watched, the great airship broke in two, the fore-part diving steeply away from the slowly descending tail. The thunder of engines, which until then had seemed to fill the skies, persisted for a few seconds and then suddenly stopped. The silence that followed was even more ominous, and streams of petrol and water poured from the now rapidly falling giant. Moments passed that seemed to be hours; objects fell earthwards, then came the explosions, two, separated by a matter of five seconds, followed by pillars of black smoke and an all-consuming holocaust. In Hull the concussion of the explosions shattered plate-glass windows and on the river blazing petrol surrounded the broken mammoth. Into the middle of the spreading flames a parachutist dropped to his death.

The loss of life in this disaster was appalling, not least because two great nations lost the cream of their airship specialists. R.38/ZR-2 had been carrying forty-nine people, of whom only five survived. Among those who died were five well qualified airship pilots, Flight Lieutenants Ivor Little, Rupert Montagu, Godfrey Thomas, Victor Wicks and Thomas Mathewson. Flight Lieutenant Wann, the ship's captain, escaped, though too seriously injured to give evidence at the subsequent inquiry. Also lost were the father of British airships, Air Commodore Maitland, and the talented Flight Lieutenant Pritchard. The National Physical Laboratory at Teddington lost its chief observer, John Pannell, and one of his assistants, Cecil Duffield. Frank Warren, one of the Cardington civilian technicians, died, as did Charles Ivor Rae Campbell, the designer of the ship.

Three of the five survivors from the R.38 were in the tail portion which broke away and floated down slowly without burning, as seen here. Harry Bateman's parachute can be seen tangled in the elevators.

Four of the thirty-two British and one of the seventeen Americans aboard survived. The Americans were deeply, some say bitterly, shocked by the loss, more specially by that of the head of the mission, Commander Louis Maxfield, who had been a very good friend of the British. Commander Dyer fortunately was not flying on that occasion and was able to return to America with as near a first-hand account of the facts as anyone was able to supply. Dyer had been a familiar figure at Cardington throughout the whole period the Americans were there and consequently was well able to feed into later American airship practices some of the lessons so heavily paid for in Britain.

When the after end of the ship separated in the air, three people in that section

Discovered in files at Cardington, this photograph shows the result of cell pressure tests made by assistant designer H. May on 15th June, 1920. The diamond truss at frame 8 and a main longitudinal girder have failed. *R.A.E. Cardington, Crown copyright*

rode it down safely until it came to rest on a sandbank, where all three stepped out entirely uninjured and waited till they were picked up. One of this fortunate trio was Pannell's other assistant observer, Harry Bateman, who on the way down elected to bale out. As he leaped out of the tail cockpit and his parachute opened, the whole section rolled over and trapped the shrouds of his chute in the elevators.

When the inevitable series of inquiry conferences had finally digested the evidence of nearly a hundred witnesses it was apparent that not only was the current state of the art inadequate for the calculation of airborne stresses in such a huge structure but it was only a matter of time before the ship would break up in the first turbulent weather to be met. It remains a matter of sheer pathos to be able to pick out strong but simply worded warnings from Pritchard's reports; on 20th July he stated "it should be clearly recognised that when R.38 was designed, she was lightened in every way to provide the greatest performance which the British airship design staff could achieve . . and it therefore must be recognised that the factors of safety have been cut down in many directions. Keeping these facts in mind, I feel that a very unjustifiable risk was taken with R.38 and *I most strongly urge that before R.38 is flown again, the question of the height at which she should be flown at various speeds should be very carefully considered and far more definite orders put forward for the guidance of the captain of the ship.*" (Author's italics).

When it is realised that Pritchard was signing these reports as "Officer-in-Charge/Airship Flying Trials" one wonders how was it possible that this rare combination of authority and wisdom was so blatantly by-passed, even to ignoring his last paragraph of the same report which pointed out that "The height at which it is the practice in Germany to carry out flight trials is also most significant, as in that country they have plenty of experience with high performance airships which they fly during the early trials at a height of from 7,000 feet to 10,000 feet." His final plea to be heard before the last flight of R.38 was in his report of 11th August, which began quite simply "I feel as a result of the third flight trial of R.38, that the height at which this ship should fly during speed trials requires discussion and a definite ruling before the next flight trial takes place." Pritchard was constantly stressing to all his superiors the dangers they were courting; that R.38 was knowingly built light and fragile; that its designed performance was for no more than normal manoeuvrability at high altitude, where the air is less dense and consequently the loads imposed by the controls proportionately lower. To fly it low and fast and to apply rapid turning movements was to invite catastrophe. That Pritchard himself had to die because of it was possibly the biggest tragedy of all.

The end of the R.38/ZR-2 is a reminder of the very unhappy circumstances in which Shorts came to finish a turbulent five-year period in their own distinguished company history. It also focusses attention on the changes that converted Cardington into a Ministry establishment.

In the period of budget cuts in the Services following the end of the war the Admiralty was anxious to rid itself of the airships it no longer needed. The Air

Shorts' Cardington designers assemble in 1921 for their last group photograph. Left to right: Wadsworth, Collard, Parker, Roe, Lipscomb, Goodyear, Bower, Knowles, and an unidentified designer. *H. G. Parker*

Ministry did not really want them either, but because the crews were now all R.A.F. personnel, subject to the control of the Air Ministry, the situation was complex. The simplest legal definition encountered appears to be that placed before the R.38 Court of Inquiry on 9th September, 1921, by Air Commodore R. Brooke-Popham, stating that "The Air Ministry assumed responsibility for the Airship Works, Cardington, in October, 1919. These works were then a private factory controlled by Messrs Short. It was decided that the Air Ministry should take over the management of this factory and they assumed detail control of it on April 1st, 1920. The Airship Designing Staff which was then located in London came under the Air Ministry in October, 1919. When it was decided that the Air Ministry should take over the management of the Airship Works at Cardington, it was decided that the Designing Staff should move to that place and that Mr Campbell, the Chief Airship Designer, should also be in Administrative charge." The inference of this appears to be that the title of the Establishment was changed to The Royal Airship Works from 1st April, 1920, and that although the staff of Shorts stayed on until the completion of R.38, they were no longer inhabiting their own factory and were only there performing a service to the Air Ministry which initially had been in the nature of discharging their own company's contracts with the Admiralty. Under considerable protest from the senior partner, Oswald Short, the company was notified in February, 1919, of the Government's intention to nationalise the Cardington establishment at a price which, fixed arbitrarily by a government department, represented a severe loss to the company.

The autumn of 1921 saw all British airship activities ended, with the R.33 in store at Cardington and R.36, R.80, and L-71 in store at Pulham, while the broken-up remains of the R.32 were being sold for firewood at Howden. Vickers, Beardmore and Armstrong-Whitworth proceeded to write off their interests in airships and turn their attention to the greater problems of survival in a post-war world.

Nevertheless, the three-year period after the First World War saw most of the world's airship activity centred on England, an unusual and unforeseeable situation. It was an exciting time for anyone connected with it, but hardly a creditable era in terms of achievement, either in the operational sphere or in technological advance. After the war Germany constructed two miniature Zeppelins within the physical limitations of the Versailles Treaty, but both had been taken away under the Reparations Schemes which the Western Powers imposed, and which they justified by the cost of the war to the Allies. The initiative shown by rapidly designing a small three quarter-million cubic feet passenger ship reflects great credit firstly on Dr Eckener for knowing what was needed and on Dr Durr for showing how to do it. Utilising wartime surplus, Friedrichshafen quickly put together a staunch little airframe of just under 400 feet in length and by clever design produced the LZ-120, *Bodensee*, with four standard Maybach engines of 260 h.p. each. In a manner somewhat similar to our R.36 *Bodensee* provided a long passenger cabin as an extension to the forward control car. This was some 80 feet long and included seating for twenty passengers, who were provided with meals during the fairly regular seven-hour flight between Lake Constance and Berlin. In the period this service was running, August to December, 1919, 103 such flights were made.

LZ-120 was then laid up for a while in order to "stretch" it by another 30 feet and hence raise its passenger capacity to thirty, as had already been done with her sister-ship *Nordstern*, which had been under construction as LZ-121. Quite remarkably, both ships were capable of more than 80 m.p.h.

After 1921, France was the only country operating a rigid with any degree of success and seriousness. The French Navy had taken over the ex-German L-72 and flown it for two years. A few days before Christmas, 1923, L-72, now renamed *Dixmude*, mysteriously exploded over the Mediterranean somewhere near Sicily. The crew, numbering more than fifty, were all lost.

Once again the airship cause took a resounding knock, yet its advocates still refused to admit defeat. The main support came from the U.S. Navy which, barely four months before the loss of *Dixmude*, had launched its first rigid airship, the home-built ZR-1, *Shenandoah*. For the first time in rigid airship history, the newly

The ZR-3 *Los Angeles*, originally the LZ-126, demonstrates her ability to operate as a unit of the U.S. Navy. The alteration of the control car into an integral passenger saloon was a concession to British insistence on compliance with the terms of the Versailles Treaty.   *U.S. Navy archives*

available inert gas helium was the lifting agent and the first major step towards safety in the twenty-three years of rigids had been made. Unfortunately, neither then nor after was there a helium-filled rigid outside America, solely because of scarcity and cost. When the British Admiralty had been preparing the design formula for the R.38, an alternative specification was considered that envisaged using helium, or C-Gas, as it was then called for security reasons. One principal difference between hydrogen and helium, apart from combustibility, is that the lifting capacity of helium is seven per cent less than that of hydrogen. This difference does not appear to be great when looked at as an all up weight of 100 tons. But this loss would have to be taken from the payload.

The traditional practice of valving off hydrogen into free air when an airship climbed became almost intolerable when helium was used instead, if only because of the enormous cost involved. Since the valves in use were frequently of a diameter similar to a manhole cover, leakages were commonplace and fairly serious. As helium came into use, the need arose to keep both the size and the number of valves as small as possible, compatible with reasonable discharge rate needs.

On 2nd September, 1925, two years after launching, the ZR-1 *Shenandoah* broke in half and crashed, due to excessive strains placed on her structure by violent air turbulence which first imposed a rapid rate of climb above pressure-height and then drove her down again. Crash investigation not being the highly developed science it is now, many of the inquiry's findings are open to query, but special value attaches to the belief expressed by the German expert Anton Heinen that during the rapid climb the discharge rate of the valves was insufficient to stop some of the gas-cells splitting. This, he considered, was what placed uneven loads on the structure and allowed it to buckle.

In October, 1924, ZR-3 arrived. This was the LZ-126, ordered from Germany, whose origins stemmed from the politico-military aftermath in Germany when the Reparations were being divided up and the U.S.A. did not get any of the Zeppelins surrendered to the Allies after the war. In lieu, Germany had to pay for one to be built specially for the U.S.A.

With Eckener still firmly in the saddle and determined to make a success of the slender opportunities, the LZ-126 satisfied every demand, and as its later long and successful life was to prove, was one of the finest Zeppelins that ever flew from Friedrichshafen. The trans-Atlantic delivery flight was made with Dr Eckener in

Dr Eckener and the crew who flew LZ-126 from Germany to America in October, 1924. The 5,000-mile flight was completed at an average speed of 62 m.p.h. *Hans von Schiller*

charge. LZ-126 was christened *Los Angeles* in the following month and then began a varied, exciting and useful career which very much resembled that of Britain's R.33.

She was operated with a fair measure of continuity up to 1932, and after that she was de-commissioned and stored until the Second World War, when the space she occupied was more important than her continued existence. Possibly one thing that makes ZR-3, *Los Angeles*, so worthy of a place in airship technical history is that she remains the only rigid ever built which flew first with hydrogen and then with helium. The ship performed all its flight trials in Germany and its delivery flight to America inflated with hydrogen which imparted a Useful Lift of 101,430 pounds. On arrival in America not only was about six tons of military equipment added but the hydrogen was replaced with helium (inflated to only 96 per cent to avoid expansion losses), all of which resulted in a new low value of Useful Lift of only 63,100 pounds.

The Zeppelin people at once began to nurture their relationship with the U.S.A., which was already moving steadily. In the autumn of 1923, the Zeppelin company and the Goodyear Tire and Rubber Company formed a new joint holding known as Goodyear-Zeppelin Corporation.

Saved once more from the brink, the Friedrichshafen team were enabled to bring about a gentle revival of their ambitions and plans for passenger airships.

CHAPTER NINE

The Coming of the Giants

WHEN the final British airship programme was formulated, those who prepared the specifications for new ships took a surprisingly realistic view concerning the volumetric sizes to be used. Although the matter was decided by the Air Ministry, the recommendations stemmed initially from Vickers whose proposals from 1922 onwards were for six civil airships of five million cubic feet. Early in 1924, the Labour Government under Ramsay MacDonald issued its proposals for the construction of two experimental ships, each of five million cubic feet capacity.

Two independent design organisations to design two separate airships to a common specification was the platform on which the whole of the new policy was built. Not only were the two organisations expected to compete with each other but, because of rival ideologies, one was to be a private enterprise organisation and the other entirely State run.

The position was explosive from the start, since the only existing team with experience was at Vickers, while anyone of any consequence to form a State team such as Campbell, Pritchard, Maitland and Pannell had been killed in the R.38 disaster of 1921. Members of the Royal Corps of Naval Constructors such as A. P. Cole had preferred to stay with their chosen nautical profession and wanted nothing more to do with airships. The experience of other companies who with Vickers had built airships had been confined to the construction aspect; they had not needed to involve themselves in design work, the responsibility of Vickers. This left only Shorts at Rochester.

Lipscomb and his specialists were, at that time, the only alternative team with the necessary background, but there was the attitude of Shorts themselves to consider. Although Shorts had gone to a lot of trouble and expense in setting up the original Cardington base and getting it running very well, their rewards were less than handsome when it was nationalised at a loss to Shorts, bringing an end to work of this kind for its employees.

It was unlikely that people could be seduced to returning to Cardington to serve the State for a second time, more especially when the prospect of success in the world of the aeroplane and the flying boat was becoming more promising at Rochester. If there was to be a design team at all, it would have to start from scratch and face up to the greatest challenge that had ever been presented to designers of airships anywhere in the world; one reason why the State-built R.101 was a disaster.

In 1923, Vickers had already formed its own nucleus of specialists into a subsidiary known as The Airship Guarantee Company, which was really a reflection of the many civil and military airship schemes then being discussed everywhere.

The Cardington drawing office team of 1925-30 who worked on the R.101. Front row, left to right: W. Hayes, J. Uren, F. Randle, C. Wallace, I. Collins, - Fitzgerald, A. Pugsley, - Dodds, - Cresswell. This picture, published for the first time, was given to the author by L. A. Speed, who is fourth from right in the back row.

Vickers had in fact already made tentative inquiries with a view to buying the whole of the Cardington establishment, should they succeed in getting orders for any of the projects under review.

With a change to a Labour Government in 1924, matters changed, and this implied that any new airship programme would mean State participation. Within a few months a fiscal assessment of new hybrid plans gradually hardened into contractual negotiations, the contract for Vickers becoming effective in November, 1924.

For three years there had been endless delays by government departments and constant manoeuvring by syndicates and alliances of many kinds. Eventually Ramsay MacDonald announced that The Imperial Airship Scheme, as it was to be known, would provide for a basic research and development programme to be operated by the Air Ministry with the aim of pioneering civil airship transport networks from Britain which would link up the Empire in advance of and supplementary to any airlines that might later emerge with heavier-than-air craft. To achieve this aim, budgetary sanction had been given for the provision of operational and maintenance facilities at Ismailia, Karachi, and Montreal. At Cardington, work would commence at once on R.33 for use as a flight-test vehicle. While this testing was under way a design staff was to be recruited and set to work in the Cardington drawing offices and a manufacturing and assembly team would likewise be brought into existence by stages as work became available.

Simultaneously, a big structural programme was to be put in force. This involved enlarging the existing Cardington hangar, the dismantling and removal from Pulham of one of the hangars there, and its subsequent re-erection and enlargement at Cardington. Once that was well under way, a newly designed mooring mast would be erected at Cardington, as would similar masts at the agreed staging posts overseas.

A review of the bygone technology associated with the construction of the

R.100 and R.101 reveals much of the actual history of Cardington. Over the fifty years since the R.101 was lost stories have gradually hardened into a single, simple, but quite vicious legend, that the flight that led to disaster was a clear-cut case of political murder. In no way should we underestimate the hazards of inexperience and ignorance, blended with ideological zeal, nor claim this to be unique in British history.

At the top politically was Christopher Birdwood Thomson, forty-nine years old and a retired Brigadier General of the Royal Engineers. He came into politics through serving as military adviser at many post-war conferences. A forceful character with an interest in but no great knowledge of aeronautics, he found himself

The world's first giant cantilever mooring mast at Cardington, seen in 1929 with Flight Sergeant "Sky" Hunt at the apex with his colleagues. The mast was 202 ft. in height and 70 ft. in diameter at the base.

Albert Hunt

eventually elevated to the post of Air Minister, later taking the title of Lord Thomson of Cardington. For six years he hovered over the progress of the two airships for which he had responsibility and constantly expressed pride of creation. Apart from routine affairs of the R.A.F. and of the embryo airlines, he had to administer the hybrid arrangements providing the finance for the building of the new ships and the necessary ancillary services.

The contract for Vickers was for a five million cubic feet rigid capable of going into commercial service with a minimum of delay. A requirement common to both ships was the veto on carrying petrol, owing to prevailing concern about the risks incurred when flying in tropical environments. The permitted options were to use diesel engines according to availability or to modify existing petrol engines to make them able to run alternatively on paraffin or paraffin mixed with hydrogen valved off surplus from the gas-cells. Each ship was to be able to accommodate a crew of forty-eight and a hundred passengers, all of whom were to have substantial eating and sleeping quarters, totally enclosed in the hull.

The airframe structures were to be designed to a proven strength factor of four, a figure later considered to be excessive but which at the time reflected the fears still echoing around after the loss of R.38. Bow mooring facilities were to be common and values were established for the strength required for riding out gales while actually moored at the mast. Most important of all was the requirement to carry enough fuel for stage lengths compatible with the locations of the new airship bases

The three patriarchs of the R.101 were Brigadier-General Lord Thomson, Secretary of State for Air, centre, Lieutenant-Colonel V. C. Richmond, Assistant Director of Airship Development, left, and Wing Commander R. B. Colmore, Director of Airship Development, right. The writing on the print is by Joe Binks. *Joe Binks*

being set up at strategic points overseas. The overall requirements for both ships were going to tax the capabilities of the design teams to their utmost, but the fundamental difference between the two was almost certainly the fact that the Vickers ship was contracted at a fixed price which made virtually no provision for research as such. It was evidently expected that with their unique experience Vickers could produce a reasonably orthodox ship based on known principles, and obviously Vickers concurred with this view.

Cost estimates for the State airship, on the other hand, took into account the fact that the whole operation was to be regarded as experimental and were more flexible.

The situation was to mature into a clash between technical conservatism and technical adventuring. With Vickers having the relatively straightforward path to pursue, comfortably reassured by its own unrivalled ability, what of those who were to work out their destiny at Cardington?

We know who they were at Cardington, but can only speculate on who did the selection. The probability is that the two Air Marshals, Sir Hugh Trenchard and Sir John Higgins, at least had a great deal of influence in the appointments. The man finally chosen to head the Cardington team was Lieutenant-Colonel V. C. Richmond, a very able and energetic administrator, a good organiser and an indefatigable worker. Lacking any experience in big rigid airship practices, he sought to make up these deficiencies by endless study and by employing the best engineering and scientific specialists available. Further to that, he made certain that the massive research facilities of the National Physical Laboratory at Teddington should be brought to bear on the major problems of design. When looking at the range of problems involved in the design of R.101 one has to visualise them as they affected Richmond in 1924. With the arbitrary volume of five million cubic feet, it was necessary to establish the overall shape to provide the right combination of minimum drag and maximum stability, and to deduce the physical dimensions that would both satisfy those requirements and fit safely within the limits of the sheds being provided. This was a considerable problem; after a great number of calculations by Richmond's closest adviser, Harold Roxbee Cox, now Lord King's Norton, numerous wind-tunnel models were fabricated and tested at Teddington, similar work also being conducted there on the size and shapes of the aerofoils.

The principles of the structural design then followed, taking into account the required dispositions of the main loads imposed by internal passenger quarters, engine-nacelles, fuel tanks, ballast, and the stresses involved with the movements of up to 150 people. The calculations were complicated by the lift distribution of the many separate gas-cells, the aerodynamic pressures exerted on the envelope by the ship's motion, the leverage and torsion exerted from the after end by the control surfaces, and the unpredictability of turbulence and gust conditions. This basically is no more than a simplification of the first look at a gigantic mechanical undertaking, issued as a design challenge with the expectation of having each and almost every aspect researched and developed to a level beyond anything previously known. With memories haunting Cardington of the R.38 failure due to weakness, it is understandable that Richmond took an early decision not to trust to light alloys, still somewhat in their infancy in aeroplane construction, and instead to rely implicitly on the honesty of stainless steel. Once the overall layout of the passenger quarters had been verified, and with it the principal members of the airframe structure itself, it was passed to one of the foremost aeroplane manufacturers with experience in detail design and manufacture of all-metal structures.

This was the well-known company of Boulton and Paul, of Norwich, and it was there that the commission was faithfully carried out by J. D. North, the Technical Director and a talented mechanical design engineer. Though Norwich was a hundred

Sir Harold Roxbee Cox, later Lord Kings Norton, left, who was responsible for the calculations determining the strength and shape of R.101, and John Dudley North, right, Technical Director of Boulton and Paul Limited, of Norwich, who was responsible for the design and production of most of the primary airframe structure of the R.101.   *A. W. Nayler*

miles from the Cardington base, Mr North made the work a labour of love, not only from a natural pride of craftsmanship but because of his Bedford origins and because he had originally been the Chief Engineer to the great British pioneer Claude Grahame White, another distinguished Old Bedfordian. All the massive girders were shipped down to Cardington, where they were assembled without the need for any complicated jigs. One of the first things to be done was to start a flight-research programme; another was to get the new shed-building programme under way.

At Cardington, R.33 had to be refurbished and sent to Pulham before the shed could be enlarged. At Pulham, space had to be cleared to receive R.33, one of the two sheds there had to be knocked down and transported to Cardington, and Wallis's excellent but short-lived R.80 had to be demolished. The partly dismantled L-71 was also broken up. This left at Pulham the R.36, in fair condition and being considered for use in conjunction with R.33 for the flight research programme. When R.33 emerged from Cardington on 2nd April, 1925, after its extensive refit, which had included new gas-cells, the R.A.F. roundels and stripes had gone. In their place the R.33 bore the civil registration G-FAAG. The crew still wore the traditional naval rig of blue serge trousers and white roll-top sweaters, but they were now civilians. The officers and Chief Cox'n were still serving R.A.F. personnel. The ship itself was Air Ministry property and the civil Certificate of Airworthiness listed The Air Council as the legal owner.

Several intriguing endorsements appeared on the C. of A. documentation:

(a) The minimum crew shall comprise One Officer, Five Riggers, and Seven Engineers.
(b) The Sunbeam Maori engines give 220 h.p. at 1,800 r.p.m. (ground level) using 15 gallons per hour of petrol and 1.25 gallons per hour of oil.
(c) The minimum quantity of ballast carried shall be three tons, of which one ton of fuel may be considered as jettisonable ballast.
(d) The maximum static ceiling is rated as 11,000 feet.
(e) Gross Lift is 59.5 Tons and Disposable Lift 24 Tons (Useful Lift).
(f) The maximum range at 52½ knots is estimated at 2,750 miles in 52 hours.
(g) The maximum range at 40 knots is estimated at 4,000 miles in 100 hours.
(h) Electrical power for main lighting is 80 volts D.C.
(i) 14 Volts D.C. is provided for bomb-release gear and secondary lights.

The crew of the R.33 ascend the Pulham mooring mast. It looks a hazardous operation, but such work came naturally to naval men.   *Ted Stupple*

Her log-books tell us that R.33 made a further eleven flights during this, her third phase of operational activity. On the first flight of this series, logged as Preliminary Trials and delivery to Pulham, she left at 06.05 hours with Flight Lieutenant Carmichael Irwin, Captain, Group Captain Fellowes, Air Ministry Observer, a total complement of thirty-four, and the load uplifted was 33,970 pounds. The airborne time of 4 hours 45 minutes evoked a congratulatory telegram from Air Marshal John Salmond to Group Captain Fellowes:

"Please congratulate all on successful flight of R.33 today. This important event definitely ends the inactive stage of British airships and will I trust be the forerunner of steady future progress."

The R.33 set out late on the night of 6th April to make the first of its several Pressure-Plotting Tests in which technicians of the National Physical Laboratory studied the phenomena now known as the Laminar Flow of the slipstream over the body of the aircraft. Sensing devices, Manometers, were attached to strategic positions on the hull and from the pressure readings recorded at those points it was later possible to plot flow diagrams to depict the changes taking place at varying speeds as well as changes brought about by different angles of attack and/or altitude. A great deal of basic data was gathered in these experiments, which went hand in hand with the study of the behaviour of scale models in the wind-tunnels at the Laboratory.

An interesting feature of this first thirteen-hour test flight was the presence on board of Richmond and one of his leading technical advisers, Squadron Leader F. M. Rope, who later would evolve the entirely new and brilliantly conceived harness for the gas-cells of the R.101. The log confirms that this test flight meandered across Suffolk via Ipswich and Felixstowe to Shoeburyness on the Essex coast and from thence to Croydon and back to Pulham via London Bridge and Wanstead. Pulham was reached at 5 a.m., but then R.33 cruised around in thick fog for about four hours, finally mooring up at noon. The complement on board on this occasion was forty; besides the normal crew there were others who had not flown in airships for four years and needed to get abreast of events. Apart from Richmond and a few of his design people, there were Major Scott, Assistant Director of Airship Development, and others like Flight Lieutenant R. S. Booth, Captain Designate for the R.100.

Then came the dramatic events of 16th April, 1925, after 48 hours of gale conditions successfully ridden out at the mast by R.33. Calamity struck at 09.50 hours when fortunately most of the crew were aboard in anticipation of a special test flight. One of the engineers, the late Ted Stupple, gave the author his first-hand account of how he had been instructed to check the security of the bolts attaching the swivel-bollard atop the mast in view of the severe buffeting of the gale-force winds. Ted was perched, spanners in hand, some 120 feet from the ground, one foot on the R.33 and the other on the masthead itself. Just as he put his spanners to the bolts, a particularly vicious swing wrenched R.33 free from the mast and hurled her away,

Ted instinctively throwing himself backwards on to the tiny circular balcony surrounding the top of the mast. Mentally stunned, he picked himself up just in time to see the old ship gushing ballast by the ton and clearing the hangar doors by feet. Only the swift action of Cox'n "Sky" Hunt* had saved the ship and its crew from certain disaster.

As R.33 continued her rearwards course at high speed, shattered girders protruding from streaming torn fabric, one after another of the engines was started up and a measure of rudder control gradually restored.

The stout-hearted R.33 secure at last in her shed. The damage sustained when she broke away from the mooring mast is all too clearly seen.
Sir Victor Goddard

Cox'n Hunt and Flight Lieutenant Booth had as their first task the assessment of damage. They had to mount the upper forward gun platform and then precariously crawl forward as far as possible. With the foremost gas-cell completely deflated, it was found possible to rig the remains of the cell and the flapping envelope fabric as a shield against further damage to the remaining cells. This was soon effected and many

*Flight-Sergeant G. W. Hunt had been in the airship service from the earliest days, having joined in 1912. In the author's opinion he was probably the most experienced non-German airshipman of all.

Men like these were the legitimate heroes of the airship era. Left to right, Engineer W. H. King, Leading Engineer S. E. Scott, Engineer Z. Little, Rigger R. W. Dick, Chief Coxswain G. W. Hunt, Coxswain W. A. Potter and Coxswain L. A. Moncrieff. *Albert Hunt*

odds and ends either jettisoned from the forward end or taken aft in order to raise the sagging bows. Fire extinguishers, accumulators and general spares were scattered in a line along the twenty-two miles from Pulham to Lowestoft where R.33 crossed the coast at a height of 3,000 feet, thirty-five minutes after the breakaway, still in a crippled condition and flying backwards.

Some officers of the station had jumped into cars to chase the ship cross country but to no avail, since with a near westerly wind of a steady 48–50 m.p.h. the ship was quickly well out to sea and out of sight. The Gorleston lifeboat put to sea immediately and shipping was advised.

The W/T operator, Corporal S. T. Keeley, reported that things were well under control. With 1,600 gallons of fuel and the crew in good heart, they were making 20 knots heading into a wind of 45 knots and there was plenty of food in the larder. At 12.57 hours a message was transmitted from Croydon to Pulham for onward transmission:

"The Foreign Office have wired H.M. representatives at Oslo, Copenhagen, the Hague, Brussels, Berlin and Paris that R.33 may possibly have to land in western Europe and request that all possible assistance may be given stating that landing would probably be at an aerodrome and that 200 or 300 men would be required for landing party."

At 15.00 hours R.33 was transmitting: "Appromixate position 60 to 70 miles N.E. of Lowestoft. Making good 35 degrees, 5 knots." At 16.08 hours she was sending:

"Position by bearing 25 miles W.N.W. from Texel. Ship stationary. Wind N.W. 30 to 35."

From about 16.00 hours messages began pouring in to Pulham from Cologne and the Hague concerning the extent of their readiness to receive R.33. At 19.04 hours the scene began to alter when Pulham was told by Rotterdam that "R.33 is now over the shore N.W. of Amsterdam." Six minutes later, Cologne was reporting "Army have landing party and mooring rig and searchlights available."

At 20.16 hours the R.33 was asked by the fishery protection sloop H.M.S. *Godetia* "What do you intend doing?" Almost immediately Booth was replying "If wind moderates am returning to England. Now ten miles south of Ymuiden."

This staggering bit of good news was soon flashed to Pulham and in turn to anxious relatives and to the Air Ministry. By midnight, Booth was able to report that he was recrossing the coast at about five to ten knots and asked for *Godetia* to show herself with searchlights. At one stage, preparations were all but implemented for *Godetia* to take R.33 in tow. By 04.00 hours R.33 could report cheerfully "Making 15 knots for Lowestoft with destroyer escort." To this signal there came the

Air Minister Sir Samuel Hoare visted Pulham to present watches to the crew of the R.33, who were also accorded a civic reception by the Mayor of Bedford. Here Sir Samuel is congratulating Flight Sergeant Hunt, who was awarded a bar to his Air Force Medal.
Albert Hunt

immediate jubilant answer from Pulham "Splendid! Signed:- Scott — Colmore — Fellowes."

As R.33 crossed the English coast in the early afternoon messages of congratulation and relief came flooding through, that which came in from Lord Trenchard, Chief of Air Staff, dictating the general tone:

"To O/C & Crew R.33. All ranks of Royal Air Force are watching your skilful efforts with intense interest and all hope you will be safe this evening at Pulham."

At 15.20 hours, the trail ropes of R.33 were snatched up not only by the official landing party but by hundreds of relatives and civilian workers. Twenty-five minutes later, the stout-hearted R.33 was secure in her shed and her equally stout-hearted crew were being mobbed by press photographers. These same photographers were later present to record the award of the Air Force Medal to Flight-Sergeant Hunt, who always insisted that he was only the holder of a medal awarded to his crew, and they loved him for it; from the early days of No.9, most were prepared to follow him to the death. In the end, this is just what they did.

Although a few months were lost repairing the damaged nose, further lessons had obviously been learned and, even though the early stages of design and construction of the R.100 and R.101 had already begun, the experience was put to good use.

One of the more interesting series of experiments carried out by the R.33 was a programme involving the release and retrieval of aeroplanes from specially designed attachments under the hull structure. The Air Ministry had always held the opinion that in time of war it was conceivable that two new ships might play an active role, possibly as troop carriers, and thus might find it advisable to carry their own fighter escorts. About a hundred hours of flight trials were carried out during 1925 under the captaincy of Flight Lieutenant Irwin, but there was a long gap from December, 1925, until October, 1926, while modifications were being installed for the carriage of two Gloster Grebe fighters. Booth flew the ship from Pulham to Cardington on 21st October, 1926, dropping the fighters during the course of the flight. An attempt to repeat the experiment for the benefit of an audience of Dominion Premiers was aborted by abnormally low cloud conditions.

On 23rd November, 1926, R.33 made her last flight. With two Grebes secured to her underside, she was led across the field at Cardington to where the new mooring mast stood. No mast had ever been built anywhere else in the world quite like it. After R.33 had given several demonstrations of the process of mooring up to the mast and slipping away, she finally set off at 13.42 hours with a total complement of thirty. The officers on board were nearly all those who were later to be responsible for handling the new ships R.100 and R.101.

Squadron Leader Baker and Flight Lieutenant Shales were ready to fly off the Grebes and two R.A.F. parachutists, Leading Aircraftman 'Brainy' Dobbs from the Henlow Depot and Leading Aircraftman Chamberlain, were also aboard. R.33 circled Bedford and Cardington for a time, climbing to 1,600 feet, then one of the Grebes slipped away successfully, followed soon afterwards by one of the parachutists. Course was set for Pulham, where after dropping the second Grebe and the parachutist, a perfect landing was made at 16.32. Shortly afterwards R.33 was stowed in her shed for the last time.

The flights of R.33 had marked the end of an era in British airship history. The years 1925 and 1926 had seen the flying of British airships at its best, bequeathing also a superbly experienced crew and above all, a legacy of technology feedback for the new ships at Howden and Cardington.

Unfortunately for Cardington, there was little new to be learned from R.33 in the matter of machinery and propulsion, the area giving the biggest headache of all.

In view of the prohibition on the use of petrol, Cardington had decided from the start to use Diesel engines. Of the limited types then available, a 600 h.p. Beardmore was chosen for use in each of five separate engine-cars, well spread out to avoid over-stressing the primary structure. The engines were straight 8's originally developed for locomotives and, by comparison with petrol engines, of a relatively low efficiency, in this case 8½ lb per brake horse power. Typical petrol aero-engines of the period had weight ratios roughly a quarter of this. The first major problem arose when it was realised that Beardmore performance was based on the assumption of it being mounted in a hundred-ton locomotive chassis. When mounted on lightweight sheet-metal channels in an airborne gondola, the situation changed dramatically. Because of the absence of rigidity it became impossible to run the engines at their designed maximum speeds due to vibration and the whip of the very long eight-throw crankshaft. The immediate effect of this was the loss of about 100 h.p. per engine; the equivalent almost of losing one of the five engines.

The next most serious matter was the realisation that original weight estimates were being proved alarmingly wrong. Having engines that were safe and an airframe that was strong was entirely praiseworthy; but their combined weight excesses created the initial trap which led to ulitmate disaster.

The R.33 prepares to take off from Cardington on her last flight on 23rd November, 1926. Two Gloster Grebe fighters can be seen suspended beneath the hull; one was launched as she left Cardington, and the author watched the 'plane crash into a ditch.   *R.A.E. Cardington, Crown copyright*

It was mid-1927 and sub-assemblies were coming into being before it was realised how seriously erroneous were the early weight estimates. Also delaying the construction programme was the enlargement of the hangar, which involved its complete dismantling and re-erection. Labour disputes and slow deliveries of materials and components also contributed to delays. Overriding everything else was the over-cautious design philosophy, demanding intensive testing of every aspect of the structural assemblies including the use of portable X-ray equipment, one of the earliest instances of such an application in situ on a large airframe.

Two physical advances in size and in shape were themselves contributory delay factors, and nowhere was it more dramatically evident than in the construction of the large unbraced rings that imparted the cross-section shape of the ship. For many years it had been customary to produce rings in a variety of configurations, stiffened with cross-braced wires similar in appearance to a bicycle wheel. In certain designs, such wires had also been made to serve as bulkheads between gas-cells, to eliminate the tendency for cells to surge fore and aft. A close study shows that no such wiring existed in the R.101 and that the rings, triangular in cross section, were intended to be self-supporting. For some strange reason, many of the R.101's critics point out that this shape of girder reduced the available gas-space within the hull, a fact which seems irrelevant since nobody makes the same complaint about the considerable volume occupied by the passenger accommodation.

There were pressures of various kinds on the Cardington team to advance contemporary levels of airship science, so we encounter departures from known practices without always being able to point to an obvious or proven advance. It had been normal to provide two separate valves to nearly every gas-cell, one an automatic safety valve in the base of the cell for discharging excessive pressures when cells were distended beyond the safety point, usually by rapid increases in altitude or temperature. The second valve, known as a manoeuvring-valve, would be on the top

The standard gas valve developed for the R.101 embodied many new features which cumulatively were probably the prime cause of the ultimate disaster to the ship. Here one of the valves is tested at Cardington.   *R.A.E. Cardington, Crown copyright*

of a selected majority of cells and would be manually operated, generally by remote cable control from the main control-car. Such a system was not unacceptable to the rival design team of Vickers, who sub-contracted the job to specialists in Germany who had been making valves for Zeppelins for years; from the Vickers standpoint, no problem existed and no effort was involved.

At Cardington, a totally different approach was made to the subject. First, it was decided not to increase the size of the valves in proportion to the size of the ship, but to duplicate them instead. Secondly, it was decided to make a standard valve perform both the functions previously performed by the conventional pairs of valves, automatic and manual. The new type of valve was fitted only at the sides of the cells instead of on top and underneath. In this position it could respond adequately to cable-controlled operation while the automatic mode was operated by a servo system using a siphon pipe to sample pressure at the bottom of the cell. The valves went the length of the ship along both sides and were supposed to operate as pairs.

Where the system eventually fell down was in the method of mounting the valves on edge instead of lying flat like a man-hole cover. This novel method of operating the valves was based on the use of light differential pressures to open or close a relatively heavy valve forty inches across, which in practice could open with the roll of the ship. Reports exist to show that it needed a list of as little as three degrees either side of the vertical for this to happen and it could do so without anyone knowing of it at the time. Despite attempts to cure it, the fault persisted and it has to be taken into account when reviewing instances of loss of lift, especially in bad weather.

From the time the first suspicions about excess weights were recognised to the time when the ship was virtually completed for inflation was a full two years. During that time efforts were made to alleviate the weight penalty by reducing the passenger facilities and eliminating a few non-stressed girders used to improve the shape of the hull and secure the envelope. The weight saved was not significant and the days of reckoning had arrived. At a time when the ship had not even been launched Wing Commander Colmore, Director of Airship Development, had confided that it would be only a matter of time before R.101 had to be cut in half to accept an additional bay. Zeppelins at the end of the war had been giving Useful Lift values approaching two-thirds of the total lift available. In the case of the R.101, although only a third was being asked for by the specification, i.e. 50 tons, in practice the figure proved to be little better than a fifth, 35 tons.

Under conditions such as these, the author watched R.101 leave the Cardington shed at dawn on 12th October, 1929. Two days later she slipped her moorings and made her maiden flight of five and a half hours.

A month later, the rival R.100 was completed and ready for Cardington, but due largely to the R.101 making a great deal of use of the new mast, it was not until 16th December that R.100 was able to make the transfer to the operational base. Much had transpired during the five years she had been building in that bleak and lonely

The R.101 on an early flight over Norfolk. Barely discernible is a row of ventilation hoods along the top centreline, intended to extract surplus hydrogen from inside the envelope.   *George Swain*

barn on the Yorkshire moors, a place whose isolation and spartan environment caused Chief Calculator Nevil Shute Norway to take to writing classic novels, with his two christian names making their permanent mark on the history of English literature.

Since light-alloy tubing of the required large diameter was not available from stock in 1924, Barnes Wallis had to make it for himself; it was to be the basic ingredient for the whole ship, and was once likened to the well-known structural toy, Meccano. The number of standard girders was limited to nine unit types. Such girders, in their varying sizes, were fabricated into triangular shapes, with three tubes forming the corners of the triangle. The tubes were prefabricated from flat strip, wound helically on a large lathe modified by Wallis to enable the coiled strip to be drilled and rivetted at every half-inch along the overlapped edge.

In most earlier rigid airships it had been common practice to strengthen the huge airframe structure by literally tieing it together with an axial wire running from bow to stern throughout the entire length of the ship along its centre line. In Wallis's design, this function was performed by a girder used to locate and stabilise the radial wiring at each of the main transverse rings, wiring that served to restrain the enormous gas cells from fore and aft surging.

Wallis used fifteen gas-cells, one fewer than the R.101's original sixteen, later increased to seventeen. This saved an appreciable amount of weight; not only did it

126

mean fewer rings but it also reduced the number of heavy joints where the horizontal girders intersected the transverse ring girders. The standard joint devised by Wallis became a mathematician's dream; the brilliantly simple interlocking of a "V" member with a "Y" member provided the stress designers with a nodal point of exactness with which to calculate the complex loads imposed on airship structures. A secondary feature of the joint's design was its ability to hold the structure together while a single girder might be removed if damaged and then easily replaced by a new one.

The process of inflation in the summer of 1929 was interesting from several standpoints, particularly as these were the biggest unit gas-cells ever used. Like the valves, the gas-cells had been made for Vickers by the Zeppelin suppliers in Germany and were of the orthodox cotton and goldbeater's skin variety. The axial girder having been threaded between the gas-cells, the latter were wrapped around the girder until required for inflation. When this began, half a dozen of the old R.33 crew under Flight Lieutenant Booth performed the exacting task of deploying the first few cells as the gas pressures came on line. Their expertise in spreading the expanding cell into its wire mesh net was a critical factor.

Still preserved at Cardington is this sample of Barnes Wallis's standard girder joint. *Author*

On the uppermost girders, Norway and Horrocks, Chief Draughtsman, were instructed by Captain George Meager and Cox'n Jerry Long as they carefully tugged and steered the massive but delicate billowing sheets of cotton under the nets. With the hydrogen rapidly inflating the cell into shape like a mushroom, there was an inward collapse of the lower half, causing it to creep along the axial girder; but to resist this, riggers sitting astride the girder gently held the fabric in the proper position as further quantities of gas brought the cell to its natural shape of a monster uncut cheddar cheese.

Running beneath the gas-cells was a full length corridor, stretching from the nose, where a drop-down door provided the entrance ramp from the mooring mast position, to the double-decker passenger quarters. Continuing aft, it gave access in flight to the engine nacelles, and importantly to the tail surfaces and the points where they could be operated manually in emergency situations. Throughout the length of the ship, internally, there were visible all the usual Zeppelin features of fuel tanks, water ballast sacks and gas-ventilating shafts, all somewhat bigger and better than their German predecessors but still clearly recognisable. Earlier Zeppelin practices, however, no longer held good with the machinery and control cars.

Like the Cardington team, Vickers were required to take the prohibition on petrol engines seriously. Trials were in fact run for a considerable period and with a fair measure of success with an ordinary petrol engine run on paraffin and hydrogen, but they were forced to concede defeat when the timescale of the overall programme began overtaking them. When it was found impossible to harness and control the hydrogen system satisfactorily, the concession to install standard petrol engines was given in time for the main erection to proceed without further mishap. The result,

A three-view layout of the mooring winches in the nose of the R.101, showing also the two water-ballast sacks which became critical at the time of the crash. *R.A.E. Cardington, Crown copyright*

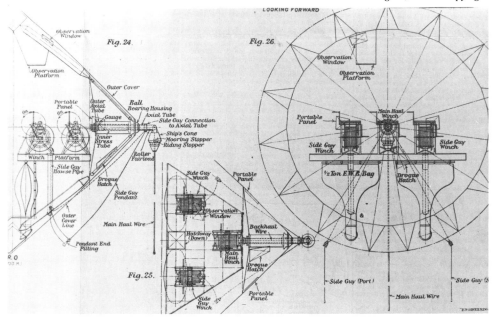

which the Cardington team must have envied, was the fitting of three tandem pairs of Rolls-Royce Condor V-12 650 h.p. water-cooled engines. The dual bonuses of surplus power and a generous reduction in weight gave R.100 a maximum speed of 81 m.p.h., 11 m.p.h. in excess of that demanded by the terms of her contract. The engines in the outboard cars were equipped for reversing, and when it came to manoeuvring at the mast, her officers were quick to acknowledge the advantages at their disposal by comparison with the R.101.

The whole function of the mooring mast was to avoid the frequent moves of a large vessel into or out of sheds where clearances were minimal. Only in dead calm weather was there any hope of operating an airship with reasonable regularity before the mast system changed matters. Using the mast did mean that many other things had to be allowed for. The mast-head had to be designed to allow a ship to swing through any angle as changing winds dictated and allow a safe access for passengers and baggage to board through an open door, some hundreds of feet from the ground, in any weather. Flexible couplings had to accommodate the supply lines for essential services, water, gas, petrol, electricity, telephones etc. Much had been learnt from earlier experiments at the Pulham mast and a great deal came from the R.33's breakaway from that mast in 1925. When the two big new ships were built, all this was taken into account, and it was to the credit of all the different design groups concerned that the eventual handling of the big ships went off as well as it did. Both vessels had nose structures especially stressed to take the much greater loading situations that research had revealed would be encountered and instruments were developed for on-board monitoring, not only of the yawing loads caused by wind forces but the rather more discrete loads imposed by the positive or negative lift of the ship when moored to the mast.

A small winch room was set out in the nose of each ship to house three main lines on storage drums, one for taking the main tension on to the mast and two which enabled ground crews to steer the nose in the right direction sideways. The position was also ideal for close direct observation of mooring up and releasing procedures, which in blustery weather became quite hazardous events demanding skill and watchfulness on the part of a team that was scattered throughout the ship, on the ground, and at the top and base of the mast. The co-ordination between men and machines was little short of miraculous and the lessons learned with the R.33 proved invaluable.

The basic procedure for mooring a ship to the mast was to lay out a wire from the head of the mast and for the ship to pay out a similar wire. Once the two wires had been coupled together, the slack was gently taken up by drifting the ship backwards and upwards until it was taut. The officer in charge of the mast co-ordinated his winch team with that on the ship, so that by careful observations the ship would eventually be brought with the cone on its own line into a spring-loaded socket at the top of the mast. After that, several lines would be dropped along the length of the ship and tethered to rollers weighing about two tons each. This prevented the ship rearing up on to its nose, but with the rollers free to move in an arc the ship could swing through 360° at the mast.

Four standard masts were being erected in connection with the Empire Air Routes Scheme, and others were anticipated for South Africa, Australia and New Zealand. Initially however, the priority was on the Atlantic and India routes. Some consideration was given to placing one at Howden but since Cardington was the Government's operational centre as well as a construction base, the Vickers R.100 was required to move to Cardington for its flight trials. With two sheds already, as well as a mast, this was entirely practical and offered the least risk of damage to R.100 which had only three feet of overhead clearance in its hangar.

At dawn on 16th December, 1929, R.100 was withdrawn from its berth with extreme caution and the grip of 400 soldiers to hold her steady against any loss of control. Squadron Leader Booth was the nominal captain of the ship, but Major Scott with his unrivalled experience of airship handling took charge of the operations at Howden and remained in charge of the flight to Cardington. Flying at about 2,000 feet, the R.100 completed the 130-mile journey in two hours and by half past one was firmly secured to the mast and awaiting the flight trials programme, due to begin the following day. As the shift crew disembarked, some took the opportunity to have a close look at R.101, the ship they had come to regard as their rival in terms of both politics and of technology.

R.101 had been launched on 12th October, 1929, and since that date had made seven flights totalling 73½ hours which, in the minds of some of the R.100 men, left them at a disadvantage. R.101's seven flights exposed many inherent faults in the ship, but they were made in safety. The longest flight was one of just over thirty hours over most of Britain, partly for operational experience but partly to give the taxpayers a chance to see what they had purchased. The flight proved that several of Cardington's bright ideas did not work in practice.

The inability of her engines to provide reverse thrust remained one of the R.101's great drawbacks. Initially the non-reversing engines had been considered acceptable as experimental work was going on with an all-metal reversing propeller, but this failed to materialise in time. As an immediate aid one engine, the port forward, underwent urgent modification to enable it to drive in either direction. Earlier a propeller of the opposite pitch had been fitted to one engine only; the engine and propeller remained as unused deadweight until reverse thrust was required during the mooring process.

One error of judgement by Cardington was the conviction that the enormous rudders and elevators would require servo-assisted controls to operate them. In the course of test-flying it was found that no such aids were necessary, and this fortuitously made it possible to dispense with some quite heavy components. This was the start of the hunt for weight reduction which began just before Christmas, 1929, and went on unceasingly to the middle of June, 1930, during which time R.100 was continuing its own flight test programme.

On a cloudless cold 17th December R.100 slipped off for its first flight from the Cardington mast, uplifting forty-five people, nearly 6,000 gallons of petrol and a few other extras including eight tons of water ballast, the whole approximating to thirty-six tons. Most of the following six hours were spent cruising around Bedford and Cardington, giving the crew flying time and experience. The interior of the ship was inspected for faults in the fabric covering, of which several were found, and the crew checked the operation of the gas-valves, which appeared to be very good. Further test flights were made during January, each covering several aspects of the programmes for auxiliary installations such as wireless communications, ventilation and heating of the passenger quarters, the kitchen and cooking facilities, etc. Problems of wrinkling and tears in the envelope in different air-pressure regions, engine-exhaust manifolds that burned out and fell off into whirling propellers, and hatches and rope stowages that froze up in the January weather had also to be dealt with.

The slipstream over the hull produced a variety of phenomena not previously encountered. One of these was the effect on crew members required to walk the length of the hull, fully exposed on the top of the ship. Normally this presented no great danger for experienced men with steady nerves, but on the R.100 it was found that at certain positions an updraft tended to lift a man off his feet, forcing him to hang on to the lifeline that stretched the length of the walkway. On the last of the January flights, R.100 was airborne for two and a half days and the flight produced considerable technical data. A number of rectifiable faults were exposed but the Government's inspectors were satisfied that the vessel fulfilled the specification, was acceptable, and that Vickers could be paid.

At the conclusion of this first phase of R.100's operational life it had made five

The R.100 during assembly at Howden in Yorkshire. *Sir Barnes Wallis*

flights totalling 87½ hours and had spent 305 hours at the mast. Its empty weight had finalised at 105 tons, some 15 tons in excess of the specification, despite the concession allowing the use of petrol engines instead of diesels.

The Useful Lift was a very satisfactory 54 tons and the airspeed was well above the minimum required. Stability and manoeuvrability both proved to be excellent and Wallis's foresight had made life a lot easier for those on the rudder and elevator helms. The provision of four-feet diameter helm wheels made the work of moving the huge elevators relatively easy and a declutching facility caused the slipstream to return the elevators to the neutral position without any effort on the part of the cox'n.

In general terms, there was little wrong with R.100 that could not be rectified with patience and minor modifications, and to this end she went into the shed on 30th January, 1930. The R.101 had been laid up in the adjacent shed for the past two months, and throughout the spring of 1930 neither ship emerged.

As far as Parliament and the outside world were concerned, the two ships were being prepared for their major long-distance proving trials which were to form the first part of the development of the great new Imperial Airship Scheme. Phase one of the programme seemed fairly logical and uncomplicated, except for the time-lag which had become the distinguishing feature of everything connected with the scheme. R.100 was scheduled for the Atlantic crossing to Canada, if only for the fact

that she was so far still using petrol engines. R.101 was earmarked for the India run, if only for the fact that she did not have petrol engines.

Though slightly overweight, R.100 was fundamentally a good ship even if, as was expected, it had its quota of teething troubles to overcome. When contemplating the R.101 in a similar context, one acknowledges the evidence that the design team lacked the same background of experience. Despite that and despite the fifty years of defamation that has condemned both the ship and its designers, no evidence has ever been forthcoming that the R.101 was structurally weak or that it broke up in the air. In meeting the strength factors demanded by the specification, the structure came out heavier than the specification anticipated, as it did also in the R.100. The diesel engines of the R.101 were excessively heavy and underpowered but the designers were not permitted to fit lightweight more powerful engines. Had Vickers been compelled to follow the same course, the R.100 also would have been excessively heavy and below the specified performance.

With hindsight, it is now reasonable to say that the sponsors of the scheme declined to accept the evidence of responsible engineers who had shown that the specification was over-demanding. The concession to Vickers had proved it, while the refusal to concede the same to Cardington imposed an impossible task on the builders of the R.101, who sought to offset the shortcomings by measures that will be seen to have been the acts of honest but desperate men.

Opposite: The control-car of the R.101 showing the engine telegraphs, left, gas-valve toggles, top centre, and rudder helm, bottom right.

Right: The reversible-pitch propeller for the R.101, a greatly-needed improvement which was not perfected in time for the flight to India.
R.A.E. Cardington, Crown copyright

133

CHAPTER TEN

Nemesis

TOWARDS the end of April, 1930, matters had begun to improve a little at Cardington and R.100 had been brought out and put back on to the mast. For days, rumours had circulated which had resulted in groups of pedestrians and cyclists heading towards Cardington and congregating in clusters around the many vantage points surrounding the air station.

Eighteen months earlier a rival to Britain's airships had flown, and now that rival was due to put in an appearance at Cardington. It was LZ-127, the *Graf Zeppelin*, the biggest civil Zeppelin so far built. Four million cubic feet in displacement and 775 feet long, she was ten per cent longer than either R.100 or R.101, but because she was in the Zeppelin fashion, thinner, she was correspondingly that much smaller in volumetric terms.

Not only was she well known for being the first big ship the Germans had been permitted to build by the 1925 Treaty of Locarno, but already she had won universal acclaim for her manufacturers and her crew by the amazing flights she had performed. These included circling the globe; flying east across Russia, she had visited Tokio and then, after crossing the Pacific, had refuelled at Los Angeles and crossed the United States to Lakehurst from where, after further refuelling, she had crossed the Atlantic in an easterly direction. A courtesy call was made at Paris before reaching home after what is still one of the most spectacular flights ever made by an airship.

Small wonder that the local citizenry waited with anticipation for the sound which heralded the arrival of a Zeppelin on a visit to the holy of holies of the British airship world, Cardington. The silver-grey cigar of the *Graf* began its wide sweeping turn to the east and, letting down steadily, came in on its final approach as though its crew had been practising the Cardington run-in for years. As the ground-handling party took the trail ropes, their efforts were barely necessary as the buffers under the gondolas touched down right on the big landing "T" laid out for the benefit of the legendary Dr Eckener. The crewmen of R.100 and R.101 formed the spearhead of the landing party and appreciatively acknowledged the undoubted skills displayed in the landing.

The well-behaved crowds kept right back as she touched down, but once she was secured most of us swarmed across the field and into the very shadow of the great ship and there watched as the crews of the two nations greeted one another vociferously and exchanged souvenirs. A deputation of senior officials greeted the Zeppelin's officers and led them away in the direction of the shed containing the R.101 for about an hour's conducted tour of the new airship.

As the Germans were bid farewell, there could be no doubt of the bonds between them and their British counterparts. The rumble of muffled engines being run, the command "Up Ship", and we watched as the enormous bulk above us ascended so effortlessly. Hypnotised by the sight of a crewman leaning out turning a huge wooden propeller, we were slow to notice the discharge of a ton or so of water ballast which half drowned us as we stood foolishly waving goodbye. Nobody would have guessed then that Eckener and Schiller would be back at Cardington within six months on a much more solemn occasion.

In the meantime, the Cardington men went back to their insoluble problems in the great sheds; had they but realised it, the answers to their terrible impasse had just flown away, buried deep in the heart of the *Graf Zeppelin*.

The two British ships were being assessed for their separate long-distance flights. After R.101 had completed its original seven flights, it was agreed as Wing Commander Colmore had forecast to splice a new bay of a half-million cubic feet into the middle of the ship. It was apparent that this would take an appreciable time, but the India flight was now conditional on this being done first. Meanwhile attempts were being made to improve performance, to reduce weight and to make a simple but

The R.100 on the Cardington mooring mast on 26th April, 1930, as the LZ-127 *Graf Zeppelin* approaches for her courtesy visit.   *R.A.E. Cardington, Crown copyright*

serious modification in an attempt to expand the gas-cells to the limits of the space available within the structure. To do this, the otherwise excellent harnesses were slackened off as far as possible so that the cells were able to fill up the spaces to such an extent that eventually they rubbed on the many hard edges and corners of this complex and towering steel structure.

While the work on the R.101 absorbed most of the station labour force, other equally important work on R.100 slowed up, except where the ship's engineers needed no outside help. Shortly after the *Graf Zeppelin's* visit, R.100 was taken inside for a repair to the tail which had been damaged on leaving the shed for the mast. Once this was fixed, she was ready to fly, the first flight to be made since January.

At the end of May, 1930, an advance party had been sent to Canada to make preparations to receive whichever ship made the journey, there being some uncertainty at the Ministry on this point. During 21st/22nd May, R.100 was away on a twenty-three-hour test flight to check repair work and modifications done since

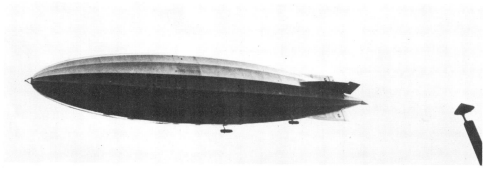

The R.100 arriving at Cardington with her tail buckled by turbulence during a high-speed run.

January and to carry out high speed trials. The cruise took her all over England and on her return, late on the afternoon of the 22nd, she passed low over Bedford where people on the ground, myself included, saw that a large section of the tail-cone was hanging down at an angle of 45 degrees. It was not until the captain was told about it by Cardington wireless that anyone on board had any idea of the damage. The repairs delayed the schedule another month as a new fairing of a rounded shape was constructed to take the place of the pointed one which had buckled in the turbulent slipstream of the high-speed run. It was now June.

The R.100 was becoming due for its Atlantic flight and R.101 was being hurried along, both for making an appearance at the great R.A.F. air display at Hendon and, it was being said, for making the trip to India in September. The question of putting

British airship crews provided the ground handling party for the *Graf Zeppelin* on the first of her three visits to Britain.   *Joe Binks*

in the extra bay was held over until it was certain that R.100 would be able to deal with the Canadian exercise.

The Hendon Pageant was billed for Saturday, 28th June, and on the Thursday, a short test-flight of four and a half hours was made. This was followed by another of twelve and a half hours on the Friday. On each of these occasions the weather was fair and did little to upset the equilibrium of the R.101 in flight, but lift did diminish steadily as gas leaked from the gas-cells. On the day of the pageant something of the true dimensions of the problem were revealed. Many years later the late Captain George Meager gave a vivid description of the flight aboard R.101 on that day:

> "For the pageant flight next day, I was detailed to go in place of Atherstone, the First Officer, temporarily in Canada. We slipped from the mooring mast at 8.25 B.S.T. and made straight for London. It was rather bumpy over the land, as it was turning out to be a very hot day . . . On reaching London we made our way down the river to Southend and out over the Thames Estuary . . . and I began to think her unhandiness might after all be due to weather conditions.
> *"The ship undoubtedly flew beautifully in the stable weather over the sea and was quite easily handled both in regard to steering and on the elevators . . .* we cruised slowly back up the river and ran through a cold front in which we received a good bump up and then down, of the order of about 500 feet, which the elevator cox met very well . . . A long high cloud appeared ahead of us looking white and fleecy in the sunshine. As the bow of the airship came under the influence of the strong upward current the whole ship was carried bodily upwards. In a few seconds, the gust reached the tail and up it went, so that the airship was being carried up with her nose down at an angle of about ten degrees. An

137

The R.100 at the Cardington mast, showing the new rounded tail section. After her successful flights across the Atlantic in August, 1930, she never flew again. *R.A.E. Cardington, Crown copyright*

experienced height cox'n or officer of the watch can negative the angle to which the ship is thrown if, after the first correction of the bump, he either puts the elevator amidships or even anticipates the tail bump by putting the elevators up a little. This was done on this occasion and R.101 rode through in good style and proceeded without further event to Hendon, where punctually at 15.50 she dipped in salute to King George V and Queen Mary. Having done her piece satisfactorily, everyone trooped off to tea, leaving me on watch in the control car . . .

". . . after a time, however, soon after passing Luton . . . I began to get worried about the behaviour of the airship. She would go into a short sharp dive, and then the cox'n would get her nose up and we would make a long slow climb back to our flying height. Directly the cox'n levelled his elevators in order to maintain this height, down would go the nose again and the procedure would be repeated.

"After this had occurred several times, I remarked to Oughton that the ship seemed to be a bit heavy. He replied that it was as much as he could do to hold her up, the while his cheery round face was simply streaming with perspiration. This rather alarmed me, so I turned on the valve to release water ballast, about a ton. I asked Oughton if there was any improvement and he said she was much easier, which relieved me a great deal.

"I think this was the first time I ever really had the wind up in an airship and I was heartily thankful when Irwin came down and relieved me at 18.00 hours . . . I am inclined to think, in the light of later events, that had I not let ballast go when I did, *the accident which finished her career at Beauvais a few months later could quite possibly have happened during that afternoon.*" (author's italics).

Further reference to Captain Meager's notes reveals that this escalating condition had become critical about ten hours after take-off and that by the time the ship came to moor up, after just over twelve hours flying, it was necessary to drop

138

ten tons of water-ballast, otherwise the ship would have sunk to the ground once the engines were cut. After the flight, Meager complained bitterly to the ship's captain about it and asserted that he would refuse to fly in it again unless actually ordered to do so.

This raised a need to re-examine the gas-cells for leakages caused by their chafing on sharp edges of the structure, a factor which had been known for some time and which had been partially dealt with by padding the appropriate places. Unfortunately, so large were the gas-cells that it was practically impossible to assess how many little holes were gradually appearing without stripping out all the cells and inspecting them minutely in the workshops. Wherever found, holes were patched and in addition, about 4,000 pads were wrapped around potential chafing points. The matter was serious enough for Colonel Richmond to send a memo to Major Scott stressing that "the result is rather startling and I should be glad if you could arrange to let me have full particulars of the positions, approximate sizes, etc., of the holes found by the crew from time to time."

At this stage, the end of June, 1930, instead of an air of cautious holding back to assess what was going wrong and the reasons why, a frenetic earnestness seems to have emanated from Lord Thomson, down through the Air Ministry to everyone at Cardington. The R.101 had made ten flights totalling some 103 hours while R.100 had made six flights totalling 110 hours. The R.100 had had its share of teething troubles, but by flight-testing and perseverance most of them had been eradicated. Possibly the fabrics gave the most anxiety and the Germans sent over one of their finest experts, Herr Strobl, to examine and to give a specialist verdict on the gas-cells, before the vessel departed on the more hazardous stage of its run to Canada. The combination of very thin fabric and an internal layer of animal tissue resembling sausage skins did provide reasonable strength and low porosity, but it was vulnerable to dampness, sunlight, physical mishandling and chafing. It was also prone to mould and fungus growth and brittleness from ageing within a period of between two and four years.

R.100 had a serious problem with a flapping outer cover which tended to let in water and acquire major tears and rips. Not surprisingly Herr Strobl examined the German-made gas-cells knowledgeably and with suspicion and concluded that another "half a dozen good soakings would finish them off". With such a verdict being made by a professional concerning his own product, one can hardly suppose that the gas-cells in the R.101 were in any better condition.

In July it was apparent that both ships were in trouble with their envelopes. Splits and leaks were taking place on both, but there were differences in the methods used to hold the covers taut. On the R.101 it was achieved by pressing the fabric outwards with light secondary "reefing girders" in between the panels formed by the longitudinals, whereas in the case of the R.100 the fabric was drawn inwards by a pattern of lacing and multiple patches.

The R.100 was virtually ready in July to make a twenty-four-hours serviceability check flight for the forthcoming transatlantic flight. Sir John Higgins held up the start of the stretch-modification to R.101, just in case R.100 should fail its trials and R.101 became its replacement. On 25th July, R.100 made her twenty-four-hour proving flight, complete with her new rounded tail, and so satisfactory was the flight that on 29th July at 2.48 a.m. she slipped the Cardington mast quietly, unnoticed by the general public, and was rapidly on her way to Canada.

Besides the crew of thirty-seven, there was an interesting number of celebrities on board for this historic flight from Cardington. Flight Lieutenant Ralph Booth, of R.33 breakaway fame, was Captain and answered to Major Scott. There were seven others who rated as passengers, Wing Commander Colmore, Director of Airship

Captain George Meager, First Officer of the R.100, left, and Flight Lieutenant Ralph Booth, captain of the R.100 and famous with Flight Sergeant G. W. Hunt for having saved the R.33 after she broke away from the Pulham mooring mast.   *Captain Meager and Albert Hunt*

Development, Mr. F. McWade, A.I.D. Cardington, Lieutenant-Commander Prentice, Admiralty Observer, Squadron Leader A. H. Wann, Commander/Survivor of R.38, Mr. A. Eldridge, Secretary to D.A.D., Sir Dennistoun Burney, Airship Guarantee Company, and Mr N. S. Norway, Airship Guarantee Company.

Barnes Wallis, the man most people would have expected to have been the guest of honour, was not aboard; Sir Robert McLean of Vickers had forbidden it. It surely says much for the wisdom of Sir Robert that as far back as that date he was not prepared to have Wallis take the risk of becoming a casualty; with the Howden work finished, what better course was there than to put him alongside that other genius at the Supermarine Works at Southampton, R. J. Mitchell. Wallis had been keen to go on the Canada flight but was shrewd enough to accept the force of McLean's logic; thus he made his exit from the airship world for good.

The flights of R.100 over the Atlantic were a vindication of Wallis's particular brand of technology and also the peak of achievement in the career of Major Scott, who was repeating his earlier success of 1919 with R.34. Unlike R.34, the new ship was well able to make the crossings in good time and with ample fuel reserves. R.100 completed the outward journey of 3,364 miles in under eighty hours, against R.34's 108 hours for the 3,130 miles to New York where she landed with dry tanks. The R.100 landed with more than 1,500 gallons still in her tanks. The levels of progress were fully confirmed by the return flight of R.100 in fifty-seven hours with a Useful Lift of 51 tons against the R.34's return flight of seventy-five hours with 24½ tons.

The outward flight of R.100 was not uneventful, since some extensive damage to

Sir Barnes Neville Wallis in his office, with a painting of H.M.A. No. 9 on the wall. *British Aerospace*

the tail surfaces resulted when the ship encountered violent turbulence over the St. Lawrence. This incident was potentially dangerous but it was overcome, reflecting credit on many people. Most of the damage was repaired in flight, revealing that the traditional qualities of the airship crews remained. The turbulence causing the damage had thrust the airship up violently in two great leaps, the first lifting it from its cruising altitude of 1,200 feet up to 3,000 feet within about two minutes. The second elevation was the more potent and dramatic, with the vessel surging up to a height of 5,000 feet in a mere thirty seconds, with the possibility of worse to follow. The seriousness of these manoeuvres was diminshed, to the eternal credit of the Vickers designers, because the gas-valves and ducts were able to discharge the surplus hydrogen and the airframe structure proved itself man enough for the suddenly imposed stresses. Studies of the helium-filled American rigids show that they crashed because they failed on both these counts.

The tragedy of the R.100 was that its return flight from Canada was its last. When it moored at the Cardington mast on 16th August, 1930, it was destined never to fly again. The writer remembers watching the return of the R.100; far from suspecting that the closing stages of British airship history were being enacted, one honestly believed it to be the dawn of a great new age of aerial giants.

With Lord Thomson pressing for the flight to India to take place in September, something akin to despair must surely have been gnawing at Colmore, Richmond and a few others who already had begun the mighty task of cutting the R.101 in half. Just over a month was taken to build into the middle of the ship the new section holding more than half a million cubic feet of hydrogen in a single gas-cell. Photographs from the Cardington archives reveal that the change was made at the convenient Frame 8 at the rear end of the passenger quarters, the new and intervening frame then becoming Frame 8a. The position of the cut made possible the insertion of the largest possible cell at the widest part of the ship. It also avoided interference with the passenger quarters.

Particular problems faced the R.101 on her flight to India because of the climatic conditions she would encounter. Flying within tropical regions, in any kind of aircraft, has its hazards. Violent storms and convection turbulence are among the common dangers but, so far as the airship is concerned, the most inhibiting factor of all is high air temperature. The analogy of the sea-going ship demonstrates the comparisons quite well by the difference in buoyancy values in fresh water and salt water; the differing densities affect the load-bearing capacities of such vessels to a significant extent, and the same is true of an airship afloat in an atmosphere which changes in temperature and density. Airships have a greater lift in cold dense air and a proportionately smaller lift in warm thin air. Little can be done to alleviate this, other than to fly whenever possible at the cooler periods of the year and in the cooler part of the day, which generally means at night.

At the time of R.101's first flights, Wing Commander Colmore had made it clear to Lord Thomson that the ship would be inadequate for the proposed flight to India. If it was still intended to go ahead with such plans, then the flight to India would have to be made during the winter and conditional on the lift being augmented with the new section. When Lord Thomson first agreed to this it was early in the pattern of events; although he was already proposing September, 1930, such a date must have seemed a long way off at the time. Thomson was politically conscious of the timing of the event; with the Conference of Empire Ministers planned for the October, he hoped for the maximum impact from the flight. It has often been alleged that Thomson's motives in urging the flights along originated from a sense of personal vanity, but it cannot be disputed that half a century ago the successful outcome of so daring a project would undoubtedly have impressed the more parochial members of the Empire Conference.

Whatever the motivation behind Thomson's planning, the date of the conference does explain an insistence on the flight taking place in September. Colmore and Giblett, the Chief Meteorological Officer at Cardington, stressed that November would be more suitable, but with September being insisted upon, Colmore foresaw

The R.101 structure separated for the adding of an extra section. This is the forward part, containing the passenger quarters, all of which remained forward of the new section.

R.A.E. Cardington,
Crown copyright

the prospect of having to fly Thomson back to England by aeroplane, always supposing he was able to get him as far as India in the first place. Almost certainly at that time of the year the air temperatures at Karachi would prevent the R.101 from uplifting sufficient fuel for the first leg of the return flight via Egypt. There was a reasonable chance of getting the ship out there at that time of the year, since her load would be exhausted by the time she arrived, but the prospects of a fully laden return were virtually nil for at least another four months.

What was needed was a great deal more lift, or alternatively, much shorter stage lengths for refuelling, preferably both. In the event, the only alleviation was the stretch modification. It is worth noting that after Sir John Higgins had reported to Lord Thomson late in July that the work would be completed by 22nd September, his estimate fell short by only three days. Knowing full well that the modification could produce new problems in flight, in addition to those already existing, it was

143

Colmore's great anxiety and responsibility to get the R.101 through its next trial flight successfully so that the India flight could begin immediately. Already he had mortgaged his reputation against McWade, the Air Ministry's resident A.I.D. Inspector, who recorded his dissatisfaction with the way things were going.

In his position of Director of Airship Development, the unfortunate Colmore was officially the technical expert whose opinion on matters of airship technology had to be accepted as being the last word. By establishment protocol and a lack of independent expertise, Colmore was stranded in a morally untenable position, having to take full responsibility for a political decision where there should only have been a technical one.

The single test flight carried out for the express purpose of proving the integrity of the new work was limited to a derisory seventeen hours flying time, and no written report of that flight ever came into being. The ship had been prepared for flight on 25th September but, due to bad weather, was unable to leave the sheds for the test flight until 1st October. Originally it had been anticipated that at least forty-eight hours flying time would be required for evaluating the airworthiness of the ship prior to considering it for a certificate to allow it to proceed on its long overseas voyage. By the time the test-flight was due, twenty-four hours was ordained as being enough, providing that part of the test devoted to the high-speed trials could be carried out during the journey to India. The log of the R.101, still in existence today, shows that she left Cardington on 1st October at 16.36 hours and returned there on 2nd October at 09.27 hours, an elapsed period of 16 hours 51 minutes.

That very same day, Wing Commander Colmore returned to London in the company of his new superior, Air Vice-Marshal Dowding, who had taken over from Sir John Higgins the month before. Colmore and Dowding both went to report to Thomson, who was waiting for confirmation that the test flight was a success and that the flight to India could begin the next day. Dowding, a man of great moral courage, declared his ignorance of airships to Colmore, since his experience was

limited to the few weeks in which he had occupied the post previously held by Sir John Higgins. He had in fact flown only once in the R.101, during that last abbreviated test. Dowding could only assure Colmore that he would support him in whatever decision he made. If Colmore had declared that the State had finally discovered after six years that it was not able to produce a safe airship, let alone an efficient one, the likelihood was that the entire Cardington complex would have been shut down at once. Not only did the airship programme as a whole have a host of political opponents, but aeronautical development itself was accelerating at a prodigious rate and the aeroplane and flying boat were beginning to show that they would very soon be the masters of the skies. Neither could it be ignored that with the world's economy at low ebb, uncertain projects like airship development were exceptionally vulnerable.

In only one respect did Colmore overrule Lord Thomson, and that was when the Minister declared that the already much-delayed flight should begin on the following day. Knowing the enormous amount of physical work still requiring to be done to prepare the ship, and conscious that the crew had many personal affairs to attend to despite their fatigue after the test flight, Colmore stuck out for at least one more day for the crew to be rested. From that position he refused to budge, and so the date of 4th October was set for the attempted flight to India.

As Saturday, 4th October, dawned, a brisk wind from the west brought with it odd scurrying showers; it seemed it would be another of those typical damp, muggy

Right: The point of no return as personal baggage goes aboard the R.101 on 4th October, 1930.
R.A.E. Cardington, Crown copyright

Opposite: Sir Sefton Brancker, Director of Civil Aviation and an Old Bedfordian, joins the crew of R.101 for their final photographs before leaving Cardington. *Albert Hunt*

and blustery autumn days. At Cardington, morale was in need of support but at least some of the tension had now gone. The day began early for Squadron Leader Cook, in charge at the mast, where supplies of all kinds would shortly be arriving. At 9.30 a.m. in the Met. Tower above the main drawing office, Major Scott and Flight Lieutenant Irwin met to evaluate the weather forecasts with the Chief Meteorological Officer, Mr. Giblett.

Later in the morning, local hairdresser and amateur pilot-enthusiast Sid Miles found most of the crew uncomfortably morose and lacking in optimism. Ted Stupple of the R.100 crew, on mast duty for most of the day, shook hands with and wished his old shipmates well as they boarded the ship. For many years afterwards when yarning about airships with the writer, almost up to the time he died in early 1980, Ted insisted that the majority told him they never expected to see him again. Among his many anecdotes was one to the effect that "Scottie" had asked him to keep an eye on his wife, who was then pregnant; he had claimed with apparent bitterness that "This old ragbag is never going to make it!"* Ted was one of those who had never trusted the "101" from the beginning, and with his veteran's experience had much earlier insisted on belonging to the R.100. On all the many occasions when the author shared his table and his confidences, he never once varied in the constancy of his accounts; possibly the most dramatic story he recounted was his recollection of hearing "Sky" Hunt bawling someone out with "For Christ's sake gimme some more hydrogen!"—a plea that apparently was answered with similar frustration and despair: "What's the use of pumping gas into a bloody colander?"

As the day wore on, the tempo of activity at Cardington gradually mounted, quite different from when the R.100 had slipped away so quietly in the small hours. Not only was R.101 known to be a political hot chestnut, but the event was on full display; more than that it was the weekend and with the "101" being looked upon as "our ship" the locals were out in full force. It would not be exaggerating to say that there was no-one in Bedford who did not either have a relative working at Cardington or know someone who did work there.

The comings and goings throughout the day created a sense of minor confusion, right from the workshops and main office block on the hill down to the mooring mast a mile away. Cyclists and passing motorists helped to congest the narrow road which had by common practice become something of a grandstand. In the town, some of the crew were having a going-away party at the Bridge Hotel where, so it was said, drinking became an anaesthetic against the poignancy of their partings.

At the Manor House in Cotton End another gathering took place. This would in later years provide emotional memories for the widows of all the V.I.P. passengers who had come together as the guests of Major Scott and his wife. As the main body of the crew took up their stations during the afternoon from the duty watch, the light

---

*Stupple was a frequent visitor to Major Scott's household, hence the familiarity given to this confidential remark, which by its implications, coming from a man of Scott's standing, is possibly the most explosive of politically hot chestnuts ever handed to a historian.

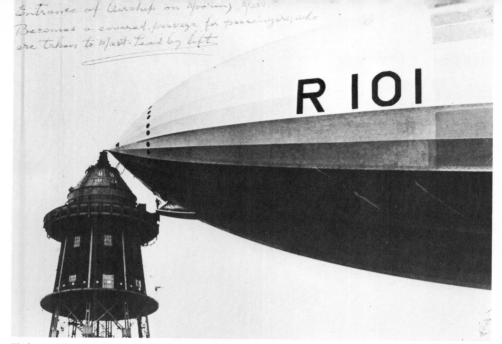

Entrance of Airship on Mooring Mast Becomes a covered passage for passengers, who are taken to m/ast head by lift.

Today's airline passengers might find this mode of entry somewhat precarious, though they were able to reach the masthead by lift.

Joe Binks

was already fading; the stowage of baggage and general supplies was nearly completed. Some resentment was expressed by those who felt that Lord Thomson's baggage was excessive, particularly as it included an enormous roll of carpet requiring several men to carry it. Eventually, all the goods and equipment and personal belongings had been cleared through the new timber-built customs shed, the remains of which are still to be seen today.

Tensions were rising and tempers becoming a trifle frayed; as the preliminary engine runs took place and each one in its turn warmed up and then shut off, pending the departure time, some of the stress began to show through, the normally unflappable Chief Cox'n Hunt cursing the engineers in starboard forward No. 1 engine-car. A new auxiliary starting engine had been fitted when the main engine itself had been converted to give a reversing facility, as had earlier been done with port forward No. 2 engine, and this was giving trouble. The reluctant starting engine was responsible for R.101's departure being delayed by about an hour, and Hunt became upset about the ship sitting at the mast while precious gas was steadily leaking out.

When all five engines were running and the mooring cone withdrew from its socket on the mast at 6.36 p.m., the world's biggest airship was committed to the 5,000-mile flight to the Indian continent. It almost failed to make it to the end of the field! In the normal course of events, a ship would rise upwards and away from the mast while the riggers reeled in the side guy-lines before the propellers were spinning

The R.101 leaving the mast at Cardington. The jettisoning of water from four half-ton sacks at Frame 1 was only just in time to stop the nose from crashing to the ground.

R.A.E. Cardington,
Crown copyright

and the departure proper began. On this occasion, the nose moved away from the mast but remorselessly downwards. Instantly, water-ballast sluiced earthwards from the front half of the ship and checked the downward motion. Something rather similar had happened on an earlier occasion when the ship had some M.P.'s aboard. The politicians had been more than a little alarmed when all the crockery slid off the tables and smashed, but were pacified with the excuse that "ballast had not been correctly distributed". That particular flight was one of the early series before any serious modifications had taken place, but when several similar incidents are taken into account one begins to suspect that the ship was fundamentally nose-heavy.

The R.101 had been laden to maximum capacity. Apart from the complement of fifty-four crew, passengers and their belongings, plus all the resources for feeding them to first-class hotel standards, there was the load of more than 40 tons of fuel and ballast. All this was broken down into units spread throughout the length of the ship, mainly in cylindrical tanks of two sizes, 224 and 112 gallons each. This was the only occasion when R.101 was simultaneously inflated to the absolute maximum and also loaded to the full design capacity.

R.101 finally got away from Cardington just as it started to drizzle with rain and began its courtesy circling of Bedford in the time-honoured fashion; some of the crew flashed messages with hand torches to friends and relatives. The author, then a very youthful private pilot, vividly remembers the silhouettes of the passengers lining the promenade rails, illuminated from the rear by the lights of the saloon and starkly clear at the very low altitude at which the ship was circling the town. R.101 set course for London, passing over the Chilterns with little height to spare and causing observers around Hitchin to believe she was already trying to make a forced landing.

Aboard the ship, with all the excitement and emotion of the departures behind them, the crew and the passengers endeavoured to bring a sense of normality to their activities. The passengers were free to continue their viewing of the route from the great panoramic windows in the hull, or to adjourn to the smoking room, where the walls were fireproofed and the ventilation an airlock against the lethal proximity of hydrogen. Officers and crew had been at their stations from the outset; with the majority of them working a watch system, as aboard a naval vessel, some were on duty and others were relaxing or having a meal from the electric galley.

The Captain did not keep watch but was available at all times, even when in his bunk. It was his responsibility to dictate the course to be flown, as well as the height and the airspeed. He required to be shown all outgoing and incoming wireless messages and expected to be called at all times of emergency, which included any significant change in the weather. The master navigator, the meteorological officer and the chief cox'n all behaved in a somewhat similar manner and consequently had rest quarters as near as possible to the main control centre and wireless room. These were adjacent to each other and immediately above the actual control gondola in which the rudder and elevator helms were sited.

Certain of the fuel tanks had a jettison facility. In the final deployment of ballast on 23rd September a total of 12 tons of fuel could be emptied in this way in addition to a total of 8½ tons of water.

*R.A.E. Cardington,
Crown copyright*

A short staircase connected the gondola to the rooms above and an access corridor extended the length of the ship from bow to stern, giving engineers and riggers freedom to move to and from their posts as needed. Two of the riggers in each watch would be on a roving patrol, one forward and one aft, monitoring the behaviour of the gas-cells, gas-valves, the envelope and any other potential source of failure in flight. For this, ladders were built into the periphery of the triangular main

The navigation and wireless rooms were immediately above the control-car of the R.101, as seen in this photograph taken during construction.

R.A.E. Cardington,
Crown copyright

frames enabling the men to reach the gas valves in particular and other areas in general. An extra rigger stood duty in the control room, his main purpose being to act as a messenger, a very important function within such an enormous structure, bigger than the average surface ship, where noise from the engines and slipstream inhibited communication.

While most of the ballast containers could be emptied by remote control from the control car, there were some which could only be operated at what were called local control points, and it was at such locations that the riggers were required to discharge ballast when so instructed. The five engine-cars were in the control of a foreman with three charge-hands, one for each watch, and twenty-one engineers, seven for each shift. Under all normal conditions, three full shifts or watches would be aboard, but for the India flight only two were carried owing to the weight crisis.

There were three watch-officers, each one virtually standing in for the captain in turn. Then there was the chief cox'n, who had his three highly-skilled elevator cox'ns to whom fell the exhausting task of holding the ship at the correct altitude for hours without a break. By contrast, duty at the rudder helm could be demanding but rarely at a critical level and thus it provided valuable experience for any available rigger. There were three wireless operators, one of whom was Disley, the ship's electrical engineer, who generally had sufficient time on his hands to double as a wireless operator.

Since the meteorological officer had on board with him a weather chart based on measurements taken at 4 p.m. he was doubtless glad to receive another for 6 p.m. which, after processing, was transmitted by Cardington at 8.8 p.m. This forecast winds at 2,000 feet over the Channel and Northern France from a south-westerly direction at approximately 40 to 50 m.p.h. with low cloud and rain. Regardless of the fact that it would have been difficult to get the R.101 up to a significant altitude, it was advantageous to stay as low as safety permitted in order to minimise the losses of gas. The additional liability of strong headwinds made it even more desirable to stay well down where the windspeed would be appreciably less severe. The information transmitted to the ship about weather changes also included indications of the timescale and changes in barometric pressure, thus enabling corrections to be made to the altimeter, which in effect was no more than a barometer calibrated to show height instead of atmospheric pressure.

As the journey proceeded, the interchange of messages continued intermittently between the ship and ground wireless stations. Shortly before 10 p.m. a bulletin was received showing that the ship had covered the fifty miles between Cardington and London in only a little over the hour. This was a very fair start, having regard to the

The officers of the R.101 standing by the control-car. Left to right, Squadron Leader E. L. Johnston, navigator; Flight Lieutenant H. Carmichael Irwin, captain; Major G. H. Scott, Assistant Director (Flying) Airship Development; Lieutenant Commander N. G. Atherstone, first officer; Flying Officer M. H. Steff, second officer.
Albert Hunt

wind from the south-west of about 20 m.p.h. The south coast was crossed somewhere near Hastings at about 9.35 p.m., the ship's groundspeed having fallen to about 40 m.p.h., satisfactory progress under the circumstances. The crossing of the Channel to the estuary of the Somme took another two hours, showing an average speed for that leg of only 30 m.p.h.

Just how much of the reduction in average speed was due to the gradually increasing windspeed is not evident, because No. 5 engine was out of commission for part of the time due to an apparent loss of oil pressure, subsequently traced to a defective oil gauge. In other respects, although the crossing appeared to have been successful, changes were occurring. Apart from the customary losses of gas which would reduce the lifting capacity of the ship, it had already encountered heavy rain which, as prior experience had shown, would add about four tons to the deadweight of the ship, simply because the envelope was wet. This by itself was not really as critical as it might sound, more especially since a weight reduction partially offsetting this would have been brought about by a consumption of engine fuel amounting to two tons since leaving Cardington.

One of the Beardmore Tornado diesel engines for the R.101 in its nacelle before the fitting of outer coverings. The tubular structure was designed so that the complete power-egg could be changed with the ship at the mooring mast. One such engine is on display in the Science Museum, South Kensington.
R.A.E. Cardington,
Crown copyright

The wireless reported attempts to gain more height in order to cope with the high ground that lay ahead. According to the foreman engineer, Harry Leech, for most of the time over the sea their height was seven or eight hundred feet. The thing that concerned Leech, as was also agreed by Squadron Leader Rope, was the way in which since about half past seven the ship had been rolling and pitching more than on any previous occasion they could remember. Leech had been on every flight made by R.101 and, like Rope, he had known the ship to pitch fore and aft and also to roll. Rarely had he known the two things to happen at the same time, and certainly not to this extent; neither he nor Rope had known the ship to perform like this.

There had already been one incident in the control car around 10 p.m. which showed that the ship had started its old habit of porpoising. The officer of the watch,

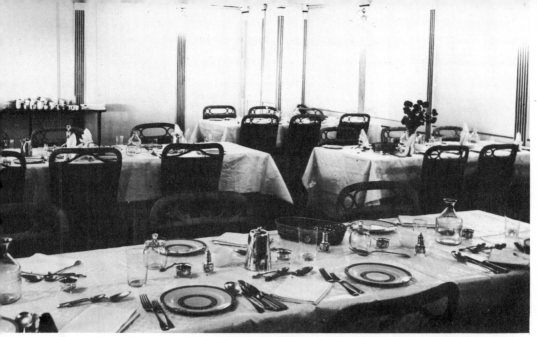

After the excitement of the departure, the passengers were able to relax in conditions of surprising luxury having regard to the standards of contemporary aviation. This is a view of the R.101's dining saloon.

R.A.E. Cardington, Crown copyright

Atherstone, took over control from the elevator cox'n and nursed the ship up to 1,000 feet before handing it back with an injunction not to let it drop below that height again. Just as long as the nose was held up about one or two degrees above the horizon and the airspeed maintained, it was possible to hold up a fairly heavy ship. Porpoising, although not unique to R.101, exerted its influence during the greater part of the flight; opinions, however, vary as to its extent. We probably need to apply a compensation factor to the late Joe Binks's repeated insistence that twice the propeller of No. 5 engine actually dipped into the sea as the ship pulled out from a dive, though Binks held to this when challenged by the author. Efforts to cope with this situation appeared to have been meeting with success, since at 00.13 hours R.101 sent a confident message to Cardington reporting:

"After an excellent supper, our distinguished guests smoked a final cigar and having sighted the French coast, have now gone to bed to rest after the excitement of their leave-taking. All essential services are functioning satisfactorily. The crew have settled down to watch-keeping routine. Message ends."

All that was so much propaganda, and the important information conveyed was that their position was twelve miles south-west of Abbeville, altitude 1,500 feet and wind south-west (243°) at an estimated 35 m.p.h. One hour and forty minutes later, the operator aboard R.101 was making his last communication with the outside world as he confirmed receiving the directional bearings which determined the ship's position as being immediately on the northern outskirts of Beauvais, thirty-odd miles north-west of Paris.

A detail of one of the pulsing vents arranged around the girth of the ship at Frame 7, seen before the fitting of a streamlined hood, and, below, the profile pressure-gradient drawing which reveals the manner in which the envelope was given devices to relieve it of excessive air pressures.

R.A.E. Cardington, Crown copyright

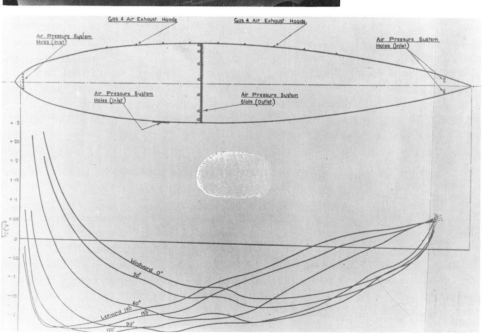

The catastrophe that followed came swiftly but not without warning. Though survivors were able to describe how the great vessel went to its fiery end and others on the ground were able to corroborate this, no-one to this day has been able with conviction to say why. The greatest experts available spent weeks sifting all the available evidence and many laboratory tests were conducted by the nation's most experienced scientists. None of these official investigations was ever able to offer anything better than intelligent conjecture. Since that time, a number of technical historians of the utmost integrity have tried to solve this riddle, one of the greatest aerial mysteries of all time, but they too have had to concede that they have little more to offer than speculation. The topic has been left wide open for writers of the bizarre.

Engineer Alf Cook climbed up out of No. 4, port midships, engine-car at the end of his three-hour shift at 11 p.m. and at once went to rest on his bunk, but he was unable to sleep. Instead, he lay there watching the gas-cells over his head as they billowed and surged around to a greater extent than he had ever observed before.

The fact that the cells were more prone to lose gas during turbulent flight had been debated by Irwin on 27th June in conversation with Booth of the R.100. He had expressed his belief that most of the losses were from the gas valves, due to excessive pulsing and flapping of the envelope fabric. Such movement of the envelope can be accounted for by a particular little-known feature, unique to the R.101. Around the nose portion of the outer cover, about 25 feet or so back from the tip, was a ring of fabric pockets acting as air-inlet valves to reduce the pressure build-up resulting from increases in speed. The passage of the air, now within the envelope, was intended to support the envelope from the interior and thus relieve it from excessive strain over the immense areas involved.

Nearly halfway back along the hull, at Frame 7, near the passenger saloon, the envelope featured another modification in association with this contrived movement of air between the gas-cells and the cover. Instead of the cover continuing smoothly from front to rear without interruption, at Frame 7 the front part slightly overlapped the aft part and was allowed to pulse above it, under the restraint of many short ties of rubber shock-cord. The position chosen for this curious arrangement was determined by wind tunnel experiments so that the "suction" could raise the overlapping fabric for the escape of the high pressure air. It was almost like giving the airship a mouth and a set of gills like a fish. To aid the process, a ring of holes on the same circumference also existed but was not normally visible since the holes were individually covered with hoods with open ends pointing aft which also helped suck out the air. Around the tail cone was yet another ring of air-pressure pockets contributing to the internal airflow. The air current moved forwards, albeit more slowly, and joined with the air from the front in making its exit at Frame 7.

Not only was this intended to relieve wear and tear on the envelope but also to purge the spaces where pockets of the highly explosive air and hydrogen mixture which had proved so lethal to other airships in the past could be trapped. Clearly this was the agency responsible for the surging and plunging of the forward gas cells that had been attracting the attention of Harry Leech and Alf Cook. Apart from the fact that the gas-valves were almost certainly opening with every roll of the ship, for they were already known to open at any roll exceeding three degrees, it is also believed that the inner envelope airflow was able to pummel the forward gas-cells in such a manner that they became little more than bellows. Every time a cell was squeezed in this way, the valves would open their forty-inch throats to discharge the hydrogen.

After making his rounds of the five engine-cars and checking that the fuel system in the hull was functioning to everyone's satisfaction, Harry Leech began to feel the cumulative tiredness brought on by his many recent exertions and decided to take things easy for a while. His was an independent roving commission, so when the watch was changed at 2 a.m. he had his feet up in the smoking room and was enjoying a quiet smoke and a drink by himself. Disley, like Leech not on call at the moment, had dozed off. Alf Cook relieved Blake on No. 4 engine-car and, after a short briefing on the state of the engine, watched Blake climb out through the hatch and up the ladder, back into the hull. Similar scenes were taking place in engine-cars Numbers 1, 2 and 3. In No. 5, Arthur Bell waited and wondered what was keeping Joe Binks from coming down to take over. He had about five minutes to wait before an apologetic Binks arrived. Bell, a sound but dour character, had served with the cheery Binks on airships for a long time and both had been through quite a number of scrapes in the past, including the occasion when R.33 broke away from the Pulham mast in 1925. After some conversation between the two of them and a few minutes of confirmation about the engine's behaviour since the changing of the oil-pressure gauge, Bell turned to make his way back to the comparative comfort and quiet of his bunk in the crew quarters above. Removing from his ears the plasticine which he used as earplugs against the incessant roar of the engines, he turned to mount the ladder into the hull. A sudden lurch nearly threw him out of the gondola; Binks fell backwards on to the small starting motor mounted at the front end of the car to drive the air compressor for the big diesel.

While the occupants of the engine-cars were bewildered more than alarmed at the way they were being bounced around, Leech was slithering sideways along the settee in the smoking room and his soda siphon and whisky glass were rolling across the floor. The lurch had been fairly abrupt and rather more pronounced than the pitching he recognised as being characteristic of the ship. He tried to get back on his feet but the plunging movement seemed to keep going on and on; what really began to worry him was the steepness of the dive, with the floor of the smoking room at about thirty or forty degrees. After what seemed an intolerable time, but actually was about thirty seconds, he managed to find his feet as the floor levelled out. He stooped to pick up his siphon and glass and replace the table in its original position. It even felt as though the ship might actually be climbing again, but Leech knew from experience that that feeling was illusory. The pause that followed was very brief, and none of the survivors later could estimate it with accuracy; observers on the ground,

A view of the R.101 in the hangar at Cardington. It is clear that gaining access to the after engine-car in darkness was no task for the faint-hearted. *R.A.E. Cardington, Crown copyright*

however, considered that level flight after the initial dive was of the order of fifteen seconds, which seemingly matched the time it took Leech to put the table and bottles back into position.

Just as Leech was speculating whether he ought to make another round of the engine-cars and check up with their crews, he heard the sudden jangling of bells from the engine-room telegraphs in one car after another and then in the control-car as engineers rang back with their acknowledgements. Simultaneously he heard Chief Cox'n Hunt striding through the corridors calling to the crewmen to get out fast.

Disley awoke as he heard Hunt's summons to action "We're down lads!" The phrase has been quoted many times over during the years and has become embedded in the folklore of aviation history.

Before either Leech or Disley could stop him to ask what was happening, Hunt was away down the corridor to alert the rest of the crew but, as Disley always remembered, without the slightest trace of panic in his voice or manner. The echoes of Hunt's pleading calls were blending with the now incessant jangle of bells as again, with a frightening rapidity, down went the nose into a sickening dive and objects and bodies fell about in total confusion. In ten to fifteen seconds, this second dive had begun to level out and it could have appeared that a bumpy but reasonable forced landing might just be about to take place; the helmsman had his wheel spun to its limits with the elevators in the fully up position.

157

One of the engineers in his gondola stared out of his hatch as he slammed the throttles to Slow and was baffled by being unable to see a thing in the darkness; there came a skidding bump from down below which told him the worst, that they were in fact "Down". Leech and Disley were not far from each other on the lower deck, beneath the passengers' quarters, but above and behind the control-car, the vulnerable part of the ship that seemed to take the brunt of the second impact with the ground, almost immediately after the first. The ship had been so close to pulling out of its dive that it had actually skimmed the ground and travelled a number of yards before it hit the ground for a second time, forcibly and finally.

A hundred yards ahead of Leech and Disley, Rigger Church sprawled in agony as the bows of the ship crumpled and the cable-loaded winches shot out into the undergrowth ahead. He was cursing bitterly at his failure at the last moment to reach the emergency ballast in the nose. Virtually all forward ballast had been jettisoned, mostly as the ship was leaving the Cardington mast, but there were still two half-ton sacks of water remaining right at the front, near where Lord Thomson's heavy carpet and champagne supplies had been stowed. These two were among the few that could only be released by local control and Church had been ordered to do just that at the very moment when the second dive began. From his station above the control-car and just ahead of the navigation control room, he had raced along the hundred-yard

An aerial view of the burned-out R.101 at Beauvais. The elevators have been moved from the up position since the crash.
R.A.E. Cardington, Crown copyright

158

Flight Sergeant W. A. Potter, assistant coxswain, left, and Flight Sergeant G. W. Hunt, chief coxswain, an inseparable pair of old comrades. Potter had been a survivor from the R.38. Hunt was heard to call out that he was "going back to get Wally," and it seems entirely in character that he should have died trying to rescue his friend.

Albert Hunt

length of corridor to the nose, with the ship already hurtling downwards in its final dive. Given another five seconds, Church might have jettisoned that critical one ton of water dragging the nose down in that fateful last plunge.

Disley struggled fearfully to disentangle himself from his bed as explosions magnified the pandemonium let loose in every direction. Leech discovered he was about to be trapped by the roof collapsing over his head. The roof was in fact the floor which carried the maze of passenger cabins above, and as the walls of his own room folded like paper, the back of the settee prevented the overhead wreckage from crushing him and gave him blessed seconds to slither out to safety.

Although the engines were being closed down to "idle", they were all still running as the impact came, helping to grind the nose further into the ground as she crunched to a standstill within a matter of yards. The No. 2 port forward engine, still roaring away, disappeared inside the crumpling structure as No. 1 starboard forward, with propeller still spinning and power on, thrashed around and stopped with its nose pointing in the opposite direction. The forward speed at the instant of impact is not known but photographs show that the nose cone ploughed a furrow along the ground for many yards before breaking off.

Back in the smoking room, as the roof crashed down with the passenger berths and toilets, the force of it burst the door of the smoking room open at the forward end. It was at that moment that Leech was confronted by the actual start of the inferno. There was an enormous "Whoof" like the ignition of a great pool of petrol

Engineers Arthur Bell and Joe Binks made a miraculous escape from this engine-car as the duralumin sheeting sagged like wet blotting paper.   *R.A.E. Cardington, Crown copyright*

and a huge searing sheet of flame blossomed out from the lower part of the ship, in the region where the control-car would have been. It was blasting flame with a white-hot core, and not at all like the colour of the hydrogen furnace that followed immediately. As the five and a half million cubic feet of hydrogen mushroomed over the fields of France, the glare of the flames lit up the scenery for many miles and woke the citizens of Beauvais, who have never forgotten it.

The stories that came out of the affair were poignant, and few of them got into print. One of the survivors told the author that Hunt emerged from the wreck safely but, typical of the great man that he was, he went straight back in an attempt to save some of his crew. The tragedy that hit the Hunt family was the fact that he had officially retired two weeks earlier with a Service pension, but at the personal request of Major Scott he went along to help out because of his unrivalled experience and his ability to get the best out of his crew.

It was 02.09 hours on 5th October when R.101 struck the ground near Beauvais; all the ship's officers and the V.I.P. passengers, together with the majority of the crew, died in the inferno. Of the original fifty-four occupants, eight survivors, most of them badly burned, were taken to the sick bay of the nearby convent of Allonne, where two of them died within twenty-four hours. One of those who died was Rigger W. G. Radcliffe and the other was Rigger S. Church, who had possibly come so close to staving off the actual crash in the final moments of the dive. It is still conceivable that an embarrassing but otherwise non-catastrophic forced touch-down might have taken place.

Many years afterwards the writer visited a cottage in the Bedfordshire countryside on a blustery October night. The name of the cottage was Allonne. It was here that a sprightly seventy-five-year-old Joe Binks related how he and Arthur Bell had come so close to being burned alive. It was deeply moving to hear him tell how he had grabbed Bell to stop him leaping out of the engine-car and had implored

160

him to crouch there in its comparative shelter while the blaze raged all over and around them. Joe believed they had reached the limits of their ability to survive; the fierceness of the heat had become intolerable and the duralumin roof of the car had started sagging in on them like wet blotting paper. Besides being nearly choked with the scorching acrid smoke, they were on the brink of suffocation as the furnace around them consumed all the oxygen in the air. With the 15-gallon petrol tank for the starting engine not far away and probably ready to explode, it seemed they might have fared better had they done what Bell had tried to do earlier. At that instant they were saved by a two-hundred-gallon radiator tank which split wide open and sluiced the car with cold water. Soaked to the skin, the incredulous engineers made a bolt for it and thus survived sufficiently unharmed to make every effort to find their less fortunate companions.

Minor explosions were still taking place within the extensive area of the wreck, and although the hydrogen had rapidly burned itself out and the envelope had gone like a sheet of celluloid, the wooden passenger quarters, drenched by thousands of gallons of diesel fuel, seemed to be blazing all over the area.

Within minutes of the crash, the fields around the wreck were thickly populated by terrified villagers. Soon gentle hands were leading the mentally stunned survivors away to clean soft beds and medical care. Disley, conscious of being the only surviving communications man, refused any form of aid before telephoning to the Air Ministry.

Back home in Bedford that Sunday morning around breakfast time, the news exploded in the town, with the shock waves travelling out in great rippling tremors of unprecedented grief. The epicentre of sorrow was the placards outside the local newspaper offices. One's personal memories are of elbowing a way through the great crowd of people trying to decipher the hastily scribbled names as they appeared on a

The main entrance to the Cardington establishment where both the entrance and the main road were blocked by local people seeking news of friends and relatives on Sunday morning, 5th October, 1930.
Author

blackboard hoisted up on the brick wall. Someone inside the *Bedfordshire Times* office was taking down the fragments of information as they came through spasmodically, while his colleague ran back and chalked up new names on the board. Every now and then a gasp or a moan would arise from the crowd as the name of somebody's husband or brother was shown as a casualty.

At Shortstown, right outside the main gates to the establishment, the scenes were similar to those at a pit disaster. On occasions such as these, the outside world tends to stop for the moment and then goes on with its own busy life; but those who have been a part of these harrowing events never forget; the tragedy written into human faces remains etched into the memory.

The week that followed was one of stunned horror, as the many facets of the disaster saturated those who were suffering family loss and those who were connected with the building of the ship. A local press photographer flown to the scene of the crash was violently sick and had to be returned home, quite unable to do his work.

When the funeral took place at Cardington on the following Saturday, 11th October, a year all but a day from the launch of R.101, it was on an unprecedented scale with full State honours. Already the French had accorded a massive dignity to the cortege from Beauvais to Boulogne, where the coffins where transferred with a similar degree of ceremonial to a waiting British destroyer. During the latter part of the week, the coffins lay in state at Westminster and on the Saturday morning the great procession began through the streets of London to King's Cross Station. There a special train took the coffins through fifty miles of cleared lines with a status equivalent to that of a Royal funeral. At Bedford South, the transfer was made

Left: Joe Binks, Harry Leech and Arthur Bell follow the procession from Beauvais to the sound of half-minute guns.

Opposite: The forty-eight dead of the R.101 are laid to rest at Cardington a year all but a day from the time they had made their first flight in the ship.   *Albert Hunt*

smoothly to a long line of R.A.F. Crossley tenders, and a new procession formed up and slowly moved off to Cardington village.

The entire three-mile route was flanked by R.A.F. men with heads bowed and rifles reversed. Behind them stood the anxious crowds; in Bedford town itself every factory and shop had closed for the day by common consent and most houses had followed the custom of drawing the blinds over the windows at the front of the house. The column was a lengthy one, for the tail had scarcely left the railway station as the head of it arrived at the graveside, a vast pit about fifty feet square. Among the prominent personalities leading the procession were service chiefs, prime ministers, ambassadors, delegates of most foreign and Commonwealth countries, and Members of Parliament. The Army, Navy and Air Force all contributed contingents, as did the Royal and Antedeluvian Order of Buffaloes which had at one time included most of the crew of the R.101.

Paying homage to their fellow airshipmen were the officers and entire crew of the R.100. One could only speculate on their emotions as they went on parade with the fairly certain knowledge that they would never be called upon to fly in airships again. Even more inscrutable were the features of the tiny detachment of men who had formed the Third Watch of the R.101. They had been stood down from the outgoing crew, mainly to save weight but also to provide relief personnel for the possible return flight from Karachi. Finally there was Dr. Hugo Eckener, accompanied inevitably by Hans von Schiller.

As the staccato echoes of the firing party's volleys rattled around the fields and cottages and the poignant notes of the bugler's *Last Post* drew sobs from the bereaved, the daylight was beginning to fade.

CHAPTER ELEVEN

The Verdict — Then and Now

WITHIN only a few months of the R-101 crash, an official Court of Inquiry had completed its investigations and had published its findings. Stripped of much qualifying detail, the report postulated a belief that one or more of the airship's gas-cells had suddenly deflated and that a downdraught of wind from a nearby range of hills had, with equal suddenness, forced the ship to dive into the ground.

For fifty years that verdict has been permanently under suspicion. Although the investigators were men of total integrity, their conclusions were not underwritten by evidence amounting to proof and they themselves would scarcely have claimed it to be so. Nevertheless, the evidence offered both by the survivors and by independent French witnesses made it equally impossible to disprove the opinions arrived at after thirteen days of rigorous examinations in court and tests carried out by the National Physical Laboratory at Teddington.

The authors of many books published since that time have proposed new and alternative theories to account for the R.101 disaster. An early familiarity with the ship and many of the crew, coupled with research and an intense interest in the subject, has since persuaded this author to suggest new answers as to why she crashed and why she then caught fire, two quite separate problems.

The banal and inadequate response that the R.101 crashed because the gas was leaking and burned because that gas was hydrogen deserves to be rejected out of hand, but one has to take more seriously the information that was put at the disposal of the investigators. By striving to match it to the sequence of events narrated in the previous chapter, it is possible to understand what did happen on that fateful occasion and to hazard an intelligent guess at the causes of disaster. The possibility that the ship's centre of gravity might have been out of place seemed especially evident at the start of the flight, when it was observed that the ballast dropped all came from the forward half of the ship. It was later established that the jettisoned ballast comprised all the forward water with the exception of the two half-ton sacks at the nose, jettisonable only by manual operation at the stowage position. It could have helped my own investigations if I had been able to trace an original weight distribution chart, which it is safe to assume would have been made before the flight got under way. Such a document would presumably have been with the ship's Rough Log, a journey book normally retained on the ship but giving data for copying into a permanent log held at base. Due to the crash and the ensuing fire, only scraps of charred leaves of the Rough Log were found and I was unable to locate any evidence in these of the Weight Distribution Sheet I was seeking.

This vital information not being available, I decided to approach the problem from the opposite end; by studying the manufacturing drawings I sought an endorsement of where the centre of gravity should be. This feature not being shown on the drawings, I was forced to make elementary calculations of where the centre of lift ought to be. Basic aeronautical science dictating that the centres for lift and for gravity shall desirably coincide, it seemed reasonable to suppose that the centre of gravity was in the vicinity of Frame 7. The supposition arose from the fact that my estimate of the centre of lift was at this point and moreover, that was where one would expect to find it because it was approximately central on the length of the passengers' quarters, the mean position to allow for the normal movements of the passengers.

We are entitled to assume that for all practical purposes these positions were adequately achieved on the R.101, in its original condition. Nevertheless, enough flying had been carried out before the ship was cut in half to suggest that if any error did exist in the position of the C. of G., it was likely to have revealed itself as a nose-heavy condition. When the new extra lift section was inserted, ideally one would have expected it to have been exactly above the original positions for centre of lift and centre of gravity, thereby ensuring no disturbance of the original fore and aft trim of the ship. For reasons of maximum capacity and for avoiding interference with the passenger compartment, the insert had to go in front of Frame 6 or behind Frame 8, which was where it did in fact go. The amount added was over half a million cubic feet, which was not merely ten per cent of the total volume of the ship but, more significantly, twenty per cent on top of the amount aft of the assumed Centre of Gravity. This would have imparted a further uplift of about 15 tons to the approximate 70 tons of lift already existing behind that point.

The separating of the two parts of the R.101 at Frame 8, immediately aft of the passenger saloons. Note the "breeches" type water-ballast sacks and the shapes of partially filled gas-cells.

R.A.E. Cardington, Crown copyright

There were other contingencies to take into account when making such a modification, so it would be foolish to be dogmatic concerning the effects, but such deduced facts do lay stress on the importance of considering whether the design change did introduce an adverse change of trim. To those who cannot believe that a ship would be allowed to fly such an important mission in this condition, one has to point out first the serious reduction in the flying time allowed on the one and only test, and secondly the fact that the ship had never been laden to the same extent as on the final flight.

From the moment of leaving the mast to the moment of the crash, the behaviour of the R.101 revealed an almost constant inability to hold up the nose. There was no evidence that when the ship was making its last fatal dives attempts were made to jettison ballast from the rear half of the ship; only that last frantic attempt of Rigger Church to reach the critical one ton of water at the nose. To have dropped ballast from the rear could only have steepened the dive.

The ultimate and real mystery of the crash has to be the situation so positively

The six survivors of the R.101, able to give coherent and valuable information to the Court of Inquiry, were, left to right: Arthur Bell, Arthur Disley, Alf Cook, Joe Binks, V. Savory and Harry Leech. *Joe Binks*

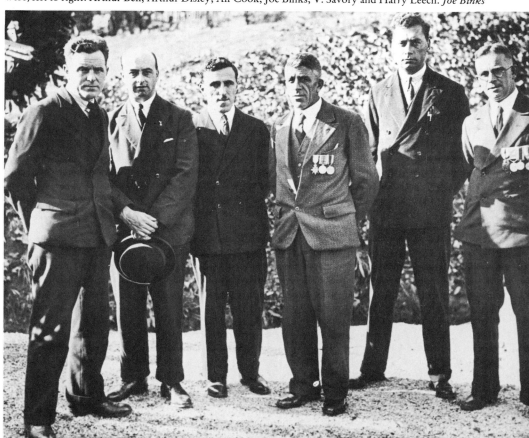

evident to Chief Cox'n Hunt when he made his unforgettable call "We're down lads!" These few words have, not surprisingly, been vastly over-dramatised over the years, making it difficult to pinpoint the circumstances that produced the exclamation, now the master clue. Contrary to typical accounts of the situation, he was not yelling those words hysterically while rushing around like a madman. I knew Hunt as a neighbour and friend of the family, and reckon that anyone less likely to panic hardly existed. The sworn testimony of Arthur Disley at the Inquiry merits attention:-

(928) What was the next thing that happened? — As we came to the top of the crest after coming out of the dip, the Chief Coxswain came to the switchboard and remarked: "We are down, lads."
(929) Sir John Simon: That was Hunt? — Yes.
(930) The Solicitor General: You say that he remarked it. Was he calling it out to notify people, or did he just come in and say it in his ordinary voice? — He certainly did not seem excited, but anyone in the vicinity could have heard him had they been awake.
(931) Was it your impression that he was notifying you and the other people there of the fact? — Yes.
(932) Do you know where he went after he passed you? — He went in the direction of the crew space.
(933) Would that be aft of where you were? — Yes.
(934) What did you do then? — At that moment there seemed to be a number of things which happened at once. The ship took up a final dive, I heard bells ringing, obviously telegraph bells, and I attempted to get out of bed.

A variety of facts can be construed from this and the first is that nobody who survived had been told by Hunt the reason they were being forced down. Whatever it was that made Hunt, and presumably the Officer of the Watch, decide that all was over must have taken a certain amount of time to assimilate. Taking Disley's testimony into account, the moment when the catastrophic nature of it registered on Hunt must have been virtually at the beginning of the first dive. Whatever that "something" was, it must have been quite positive and irrevocable. With the ship at that time flying at 1,500 feet above sea level, 1,200 feet above the ground, it seems inconceivable that the command officers at that moment abandoned all hope because of the wind which the Court suggested had driven the ship forcibly into the ground.

What other evidence was there that could even suggest other forms of sudden crisis? At the scene of the wreck it was found that the elevators were in the maximum up position, perfectly logical until someone found one of the elevator cables was broken. This created consternation until laboratory tests proved indisputably that it had broken after the impact, not before.

We may discard other typical possibilities, as for example the theory of structural failure, which we reject in the knowledge that the ship was overweight because it was too strong. We eliminate too, any question of a fire on board, electrical or otherwise, simply because it would have consumed the entire ship in a matter of seconds. Contrary to ill-informed accounts, all five engines were cruising sweetly enough and the ship's airspeed of about 55 knots was entirely satisfactory. Fuel

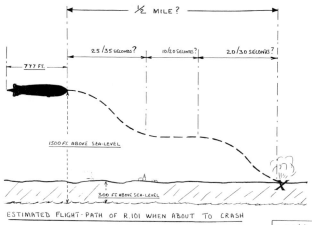

The author's reconstruction of R.101's probable flight-path immediately before the crash.

consumption was on the high side, due to unfavourable winds, but at the same time, over 6,000 gallons had been taken aboard and shortages were not imminent.

Since there was no reason in 1930 to consider sabotage, nor was any indication found, we have nothing left to consider as faulty but the gas-cells and envelope. Any evidence of the state of the envelope would have been obliterated by fire, but it is worth remembering that there are many records of quite serious envelope damage being repaired in flight. When we consider the gas-cells and their valves, not only are we in the more probable area of critical failures, but the amount of information available is plentiful to the point of bewilderment. Research has revealed an enormous amount of data to support a hypothesis that the last flight of the R.101 was performed in a condition that entailed steady gas leakages in the forward cells, leading to their ultimate and final collapse.

Deflation and gas losses are topics we seem to have encountered at almost every phase in the life of the R.101; Leech was even discussing it with Irwin, the Captain of R.101, during its last flight. George Meager had complained about it bitterly after he had come close to crashing the ship between Luton and Cardington. There was no doubt that gas losses were a problem, but they manifested themselves in many ways and these were the sort of issues the Court went to some trouble to investigate.

Undue significance was given to a report that during its early life the ship was losing about 22,000 cubic feet of gas daily. This is one of those odd statistics which sound dramatic but which in context are negligible. Writers have quoted this figure with monotonous regularity, but when it is related to the complete volume of the ship it represents no more than a half of one per cent. Why anyone ever bothered to mention it is a mystery, when it is remembered that wartime Zeppelins often got back to Germany safely with as little as half their hydrogen.

The whole subject of gas losses was ranged over at some length by the inquiry, but the vital ingredient which could have revealed the extent of losses through the valves was never declared. It was accepted that the valves were unduly sensitive and that they were at their worst when the ship rolled in turbulence, but the severity of the effect lacked the certainty of measurement. After many days of studying the Minutes of the Inquiry, I was at a loss to account for an absence of detail showing either how much gas was believed to have been lost over the whole period the ship had been at Cardington or alternatively how much gas had actually been pumped into her in that same time. My subsequent search of archive material revealed information which, so far as I can establish, never came to the attention of the Court.

The document in question is the Work Log for the R.101. The fact that it covers only the very early flying period of the ship, from its first flight of 14th October, 1929, through to its return to the hangar at the end of November, may have made it seem irrelevant to the crash of a year later. On the other hand, the entries reveal that quite massive amounts of gas were being consumed to make up for losses in the six-week period when R.101 was at the mast after the launching; a time when all the equipment was new and before the cells became perforated by chafing after the netting had been let out. Not only does it contain constant references to inspections and repairs to various of the gas-cells and their valves, such as No. 4 cell being deflated to 60 per cent before a piece of dirt was found holding the valve open, but it records gas supplies that make the figure of 22,000 cubic feet look absurd.

The quantities listed give support to reports that the valves were known to open when the ship was rolling at the mast. It can be seen that quite large amounts were needed almost daily for about six weeks, while an astonishing total of three million cubic feet was used overall.

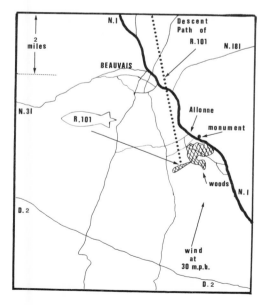

A sketch-map of the Beauvais district showing the crash site.

DATE	GAS SUPPLIED	FLYING TIME	REMARKS
Oct. 14th 1929	49,200 cu. ft.	5½ hours	Gassed all bags to 95%
15th	No Record		Gassed all bags to 95%
16th	No Record		—
17th	No Record		Gassed all bags to 96%
18th	No Record	9½ hours	—
19th	No Record		Inspected gas valves and controls
20th	No Record		Bags rubbing at 5–9–10
21st	118,600 cu. ft.		Gassed all bags to 97%
22nd	279,600 cu. ft.		Gassed all bags to 97%
23rd	No Record		—
24th	No Record		
25th	77,900 cu. ft.		Gassed all bags to 97%
26th	No Record		
27th	No Record		Inspection by D.O. & D.C.
28th	No Record		Inspecting tail
29th	137,800 cu. ft.		Gassed all bags to 97%
30th	164,800 cu. ft.		Gassed all bags to 97%
31st	No Record		—
Nov. 1st 1929	348,000 cu. ft.	7 hours	Gassed all bags to 97%
2nd	No Record	14 hours	—
3rd	354,000 cu. ft.		Gassed all bags to 95%
4th	No Record		—
5th	No Record		
6th	89,000 cu. ft.		Gassed all bags to 97%
7th	No Record		—
8th	No Record	3 hours	
9th	102,000 cu. ft.		Gassed all bags to 93%
10th	No Record		—
11th	158,000 cu. ft.		Gassed all bags to 93%
12th	326,000 cu. ft.		Gassed all bags to 96%
13th	181,000 cu. ft.		Gassed all bags to 97%
14th	No Record	3 hours	—
15th	225,700 cu. ft.		
16th	97,000 cu. ft.		Gassed all bags to 97%
17th	148,000 cu. ft.	30 hours	Gassed all bags to 97%
18th	326,600 cu. ft.		Gassed all bags to 95%
19th	83,000 cu. ft.		—
20th	58,000 cu. ft.		
21st	119,000 cu. ft.		Gassed all bags to 95%
22nd	No Record		—
23rd	102,000 cu. ft.		Gassed all bags to 97%
24th	157,000 cu. ft.		Gassed all bags to 97%
25th	No Record		
26th	132,000 cu. ft.		Gassed all bags to 97%
27th	No Record		—
28th	No Record		
29th	82,000 cu. ft.		Gassed all bags to 98%
30th	Left mast at 4.50 p.m. and entered shed at 6.30 p.m.		

The figures in the above table speak for themselves and little more need be said than that the conditions they portray can scarcely have improved. On two flights made on the 1st and 14th of November as the ship was leaving the mast it was found necessary to valve off gas from the after-end cells 12, 13 and 14. There is no record of the jettisoning of ballast from the forward end, but it will be seen that an out of trim condition had been encountered on the third flight of the R.101, within a fortnight of its original launching.

More than enough data has been examined to reveal a steadily deteriorating condition that stubbornly resisted every effort to eliminate it. A study of the way the cells behaved as they continued to deflate during flight throws further light on the matter. For this information I am grateful to acknowledge having had access to the papers of the late Newman Alcock, Secretary of the Glasgow branch of the Royal Aeronautical Society, well known for his extensive studies of British airships and in particular for his scientific appraisal of R.101's gas-cell behaviour pattern. He was especially concerned to establish the extent of the surging phenomenon.

After taking into account the absence of inter-cell bulkhead wiring and the fact of the cell harness having been relaxed, he calculated that fore-and-aft surging could approximate to ten per cent of the cell diameter. Since this could result in a surge of nearly 14 feet, he was further convinced that repeated surging caused pulsing pressures within the cells that triggered the ultra-sensitive valves and brought on a progressive deflation.

With this as a reasonable hypothesis of what was happening inside the R.101 as it porpoised and corkscrewed its way across the English Channel, it is not hard to imagine Hunt's early concern for his gas-contents growing into a conviction that the ship could not remain airborne. Almost certainly his riggers, performing their vigilant patrols within the structure, would have been keeping him informed of the changing conditions they saw by the light of their torches. Hunt, with all his vast experience, was not the type of man to have taken his eye off a situation of this sort during the hours that followed their departure from Cardington. In particular, he knew how unreliable the gas-valves were, having earlier put in a serious written complaint about them.

In short, all the possibilities we have examined share a common potential of slowly but steadily inducing partial deflation of the gas-cells, almost certainly in the fore part of the ship. Here, we need to place stress on the word "partial", because when we give careful attention to the timescale of the happenings we remind ourselves that Hunt knew quite definitely that the end had come, when the ship was still at a safe altitude. It is impossible to believe that Hunt knew the ship to be doomed because of partial deflation. Neither could he have been so sure if he had wondered if the wind was going to destroy the ship.

Only one positive calamity could have made Hunt so certain, and that would have been not the partial deflation of several cells but their total collapse. The major splitting of several cells simultaneously could have produced such a situation, but the manner of such a happening is far from easy to explain. In the mind of the author there exists an image of the immense flaccid billowing cells, over 40 yards in diameter, surging forwards and backwards like huge sails until with a knock-on effect, like a row of dominoes, two, three, perhaps four cells wrenched themselves free from the gas-valves supported by the main structure. Fabric seals secured the valves to the cells with rubber solution; however stoutly made, the seals would have been hard pressed not to yield to forces of this kind.

The next logical step was to reconstruct the witnesses' reports describing the nature of R.101's dive to destruction. This has now been interpreted into diagrammatic form, possibly for the first time. What it has to show in particular is a pattern of descent indicative of a massively nose-heavy condition. It is safe to assume that as it took place full elevator control was being applied, but it was ineffective at normal speed. As the nose fell away into the first dive, the airspeed rose rapidly,

The way in which the winches were catapulated out of the nose demonstrates the velocity of the R.101 at the time she crashed. Clearly her speed was much in excess of contemporary estimates.

R.A.E. Cardington,
Crown copyright

making the elevators effective enough to pull the ship out of the dive for a few seconds. As the speed fell away again and elevator power with it, down went the nose into a second dive, building up speed yet again and, as before, restoring elevator power and raising the nose for the second time. That was the point at which young Church was so frantically struggling to rid the ship of that lethal ton of ballast on the nose.

Rigger Church died from his burns, but the fact that he was not killed outright in the impact shows that R.101 did not dive straight into the ground. The nose pyramid structure gouged a furrow along the ground for several yards and then broke up, pitching the winches off their pedestals. Some of the best accounts written about the event by responsible writers have concluded that the ship touched down at a speed as low as 5 m.p.h. and then, having bounced lightly, skipped to a stop a few seconds later and a few yards further on. This may well be considered an underestimate, even allowing for the ship being head to wind; it was only just pulling out from a steep dive and all the available evidence points to the probability that impact took place at an angle of approximately 20 degrees to the horizontal.

Drawings made at the scene revealed that the structure telescoped by approximately one hundred feet, a degree of damage more in accordance with a speed of 40 m.p.h. or possibly more.

Sketches made by the author, offered as an interpretation of the survivors' descriptions of the crash, show that the tail stayed high at first before coming to rest with the rudder-post hitting the ground fairly hard and crumpling as the rudder also came away from its hinges. Official drawings of the crash, found in archive material long after the author made his sketches based on verbal reports, bear a striking similarity to the author's sketches and thus give credence to the accuracy of the verbal reports.

There was no trace of fire having begun before the ship crashed, and it is therefore certain that casualties would have been light indeed had not fire occurred subsequently. How the fire began is yet another major mystery. It is a popular

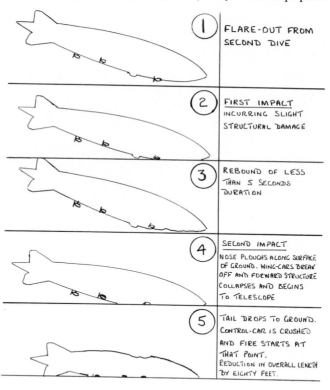

The author's interpretation of survivors' reports of the various phases of the crash of the R.101.

① FLARE-OUT FROM SECOND DIVE

② FIRST IMPACT INCURRING SLIGHT STRUCTURAL DAMAGE

③ REBOUND OF LESS THAN 5 SECONDS DURATION

④ SECOND IMPACT NOSE PLOUGHS ALONG SURFACE OF GROUND. WING-CARS BREAK OFF AND FORWARD STRUCTURE COLLAPSES AND BEGINS TO TELESCOPE

⑤ TAIL DROPS TO GROUND. CONTROL-CAR IS CRUSHED AND FIRE STARTS AT THAT POINT. REDUCTION IN OVERALL LENGTH BY EIGHTY FEET.

SEQUENCES IN THE CRASH OF THE R.101 ———
(AS DEDUCED FROM THE RECORDED EVIDENCE OF WITNESSES)

G.A.C. 29/9/80

173

misconception that whenever a hydrogen-filled rigid airship crashes, it must of necessity burn. That is a myth, with many case-histories on record to illustrate the contrary. It is a dictum well known to modern air crash investigators that total catastrophe rarely stems from a single original cause; almost invariably it is the existence of two unfortunate conditions simultaneously that converts a bad situation into an impossible one. I believe that the burning of the R.101 was brought about by human error, compounded by an unforeseeable situation in which a unique design feature made itself the catalyst of destruction in a way that could not have occurred in any previous rigid.

Many causes have been advanced over the years, some of them silly and some not so silly, as for example the fracture of current-carrying electrical cables. Disley was actually tripping circuit-breakers just as the ship crashed, essentially because he

The master-controls for the electrical power distribution in the midships area of the R.101's belly. Disley had isolated these circuits before the moment of impact and escaped before the hull came down to crush this installation into the ground.
R.A.E. Cardington, Crown copyright

was well aware of the risk. Could there have been sparks generated by the fracture of metal being bent or crushed during the crash? It is not widely known that each of the five engines had petrol tanks for the starting motors. Could that petrol have been ignited by sparks? Did the gas-cell fabrics themselves rip, and in the process generate static electricity?

Since none of these causes was capable of proof, what else is there which might be deduced from the testimony of the few who survived? Surely there must have been priceless clues in the first-hand statements of the men who had been the closest to the start of the conflagration? Consider the information extracted from Alf Cook:

(681) Just one more question. You spoke of an explosion when the vessel struck the ground for the second time. Do you remember that? — Yes.

(682) Combustion, very very rapid combustion, is not quite the same as an explosion, but an engineer is a better judge of that than most people. When you say that it was an explosion, can you give us any help as to what kind of noise it was, what sort of thing it was?—It was a kind of rumbling sound, like a long drawn out sound, a rumbling sound.

(683)A long drawn out rumbling sound? — Yes.
The witness withdrew.

Other facts came out during the interrogation of Harry Leech:

(750) Very soon after the impact, was there a flame or fire? — Yes.
(751) About how long after? — I should say simultaneously with the impact, the lights went out and within perhaps a second there was a flash of flame.
(752) Was there any explosion? — Not a violent explosion, but just a "whoof" rather similar to igniting petrol which has been poured on to the floor or something like that. There was no concussion with it.
(753) You told us there was a flash of flame. Did that accompany what you call the explosion? — Yes.
(754) Could you see at all, or form any opinion, as to where the flame originated? — Yes. The smoking-room door swung open and it appeared to originate from over the control car, but of course I could not say whether the flame had drifted down from the forward end of the ship or not.
(755) You say that the door came open? — Yes, it swung back. It was hinged on its forward end and it swung back against the forward bulkhead.
(756) It was through the door that you saw the flames? — Yes.
(757) As you say, you cannot say whether they originated there, but they were coming from that direction? — Yes.
(758) What happened after that? — There is one thing which I should like to say about the flame which impressed me at the time. I do not think I put it in my statement. What impressed me was the colour of it. It was very white, and not at all like a hydrogen flame.
(759)At this moment you were still seated on the settee; is that right? — Yes. At the moment of the flash, or explosion, whichever you like to call it, I jumped off the settee.
(760) What else can you tell me? — I could not jump off to my full height, because the upper deck had shut down on the top of the settee. I could only more or less rise about 4 feet.
(761) Did the flame come into that space? — No, there was no flame at all in the smoking room, but thick choking smoke.
(762) I think that you heard people screaming and shouting? — I would rather not refer to that.

Continued studies of the investigation minutes throw up intriguing accounts of this kind which suggest a common link of some kind. Harry Leech, when he was being questioned about his presence in the control car about ten o'clock when Commander Atherstone as Officer of the Watch had been reprimanding the elevator cox'n for not keeping sufficient height, was asked whether any drift readings had been taken during that time. He confirmed that Squadron Leader Johnston had been doing them with the aid of calcium flares, which when they were dropped into the sea were self igniting. In the daytime their smoke trail gave a first-class visible marker while at night a searing white flame proved just as effective. With two or more in line, a navigator was able to check the amount of drift.

(901) . . . As a matter of fact, judging by the box that he had on the floor, I should say that he had used seven, because I think the box held a dozen and there were only five in it.
(902) The Solicitor General: Where was Major Johnston?—In the control car in the after position.

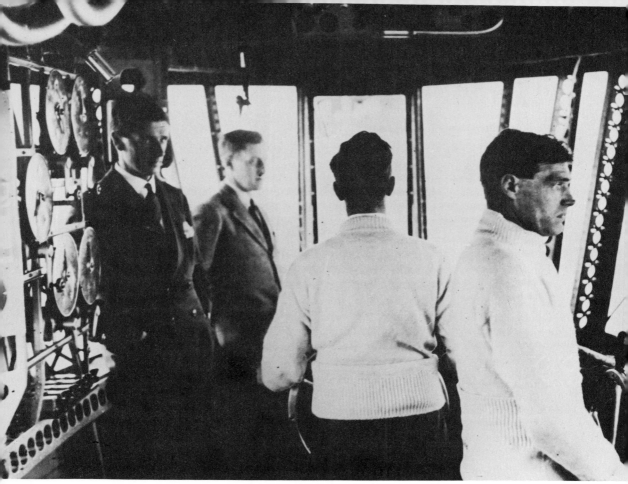

Looking forward in the control-car of the R.101, with, left to right, Flight Lieutenant Irwin, Lieutenant Commander Atherstone, Flight Sergeant Potter and Flight Sergeant Hunt. The elevator coxswain at the helm on the starboard side would normally have access to the ballast controls set close to his right hand.

R.A.E. Cardington, Crown copyright

(903) In the car itself below the room? — Yes. Immediately at the bottom of the companion ladder.

I claim no originality for having suspected the presence of the flares as the cause of the fire, but up to the time of writing nobody seems to have explained how the flares ignited. These flares consisted of five pounds of calcium-phosphide contained in a perforated cardboard cylinder to allow the penetration of water. Either salt water or fresh would trigger an intense blaze that would burn with a white light for about thirty-seconds.

How could enough water have got into the open box of calcium flares, declared to have been left in the control-car in that condition, to have ignited them? I went again to the original manufacturing drawings, and there I found an answer I could never have envisaged after many years of studying orthodox Zeppelins and earlier British airships.

The General Arrangement Drawing for the water-ballast storage and control system revealed an installation quite unlike anything I had ever encountered before. There, in stark simplicity, was a vast supply of cold water piped into the control-car, right next to where Leech had seen the box of flares with the lid off. Instead of the conventional panel of toggles over the cox'n's head for remotely jettisoning individual ballast sacks up in the hull, three separate wheel-valves were mounted on the starboard wall of the car. They were in the supply-line pipes coming down through the roof from a main water supply stretching right from the mooring attachment on the nose, along the length of the ship and tee-ing off at intervals into the ballast points, thus enabling them all to be filled up through a single hose-coupling at the front. Positioned closely together, but connecting separately into this large single main, were two aluminium pipes of two and a half inches bore. Separating their joints in the main line by a simple stop-cock ensured that the two pipes provided direct but independent feeds from either the front half or the rear half of the water system. The two pipes led vertically down into the cabin, where each separate feed could be released by its own valve; after that both feeds led into a single pipe discharging out through the floor of the cabin, but not before it was permitted to do so by the third wheel valve placed in that line. All told, it was a simple and entirely novel arrangement and had a great deal to commend it.

The external supply of water would be pumped into the airship through the hose connection in the nose cone. With the general supply cocks open all along the pipeline system, the incoming water would progressively fill up all the main ballast

The memorial at Allonne, near Beauvais, to those who died in the R.101. A smaller tablet has been placed on the actual crash site. *Author*

tanks, most of which could be emptied subsequently by the system we have just described as existing in the control car. For reasons that are not easily apparent, some of the ballast could only be released in situ. It is clear that by shutting off the mid-position stop-cock after filling was completed, those in the control-car were

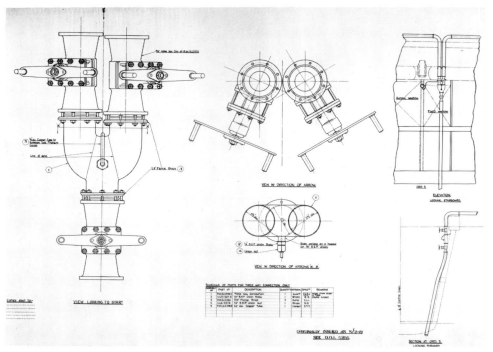

A General Arrangement drawing of the Ballast Jettison Control in the R.101, showing the departure from tradition which was probably responsible for the destruction of the ship by fire.

R.A.E. Cardington, Crown copyright

provided with a valuable quick-trim system for normal fore and aft balance. By opening all three valves, they could jettison all the main ballast.

What nobody could ever have foreseen was the likelihood of somebody having neglected to cover up a half-used box of flares. Nor could they have taken into account that when the ship crashed, those soft aluminium pipes of 2½ inches diameter would have ruptured, flooding a control-car being flattened under the weight of the overhead wreckage. Water to ignite those flares was present in abundance.

CHAPTER TWELVE

Sic Transit Gloria

R IGID airship history between the two world wars was marred by unforgettable tragedies beginning with the British R.38 of 1921 and continuing with the French *Dixmude* in 1923, the American *Shenandoah* in 1925 and the R.101 in 1930. The loss of life was considerable in each case, and worse was to come in the following decade.

Although no lives were lost with R.33 and R.34, we have already seen that both these ships had come exceedingly close to disaster. The brilliant record of the two Zeppelins LZ-126 and LZ-127 provided a scintillating contrast. The whole of their operational lives was a testimony to the German mastery of the profession at Friedrichshafen, and it was no mere coincidence that both survived till they were dismantled during the Second World War. How could one possibly contemplate the services rendered by these two ships and simultaneously condemn the concept of the rigid, as many people did then and do now?

Their successes were all the more important because they were not only operated by different nationalities and in different countries, but their functional roles were so essentially different. LZ-126 was the naval-military ship *Los Angeles* and the other was the civil-operated *Graf Zeppelin*, destined to become known as the most successful globe-trotting airship ever built.

It was technical superiority which ensured the permanence of the fame so well earned by the *Graf Zeppelin*. One other less well known fact contributed to the success of LZ-127. The new 12-cylinder Maybach engines, five of which powered the *Graf Zeppelin*, were able to run either on petrol or on gas of the natural methane variety, known to the Germans as "Blaugas". This was not even regarded as an emergency fuel, since enough was carried on board to provide an endurance of at least 100 hours flying time. It was stored in an identical manner to the lifting hydrogen which occupied gas-cells in the upper two-thirds of the ship. The fuel gas, at atmospheric pressure, occupied similar gas-cells in the lower one-third of the hull.

Altogether the *Graf Zeppelin* displaced four million cubic feet of air, but of this about three millions was the lifting hydrogen and the remainder was fuel gas. Two main virtues resulted from this novel installation. First, the consumption of fuel gas did not affect the trim of buoyancy of the ship throughout the duration of the flight, because the weight of the gas was only slightly different from that of the air it displaced. Secondly, if the space used by the fuel gas had been used by hydrogen instead, thirty extra tons of lift could have carried thirty tons of petrol, but that amount of petrol would only have propelled the airship for two-thirds of the distance achieved by "Blaugas". Because this unique system ensured consistent cruising altitudes, the waste of ballast and of hydrogen was greatly reduced, thus conferring immense operational advantages. Had such a system been perfected on the British R.100 and R.101, air history must have taken a different course.

The loss of R.101 by hydrogen fire did, however, condition the thinking of the Zeppelin designers, especially since Friedrichshafen was then engaged on new feasibility studies for a ship not very much bigger than the R.101 itself. The Germans had been no strangers to hydrogen fires during wartime, but they were shrewd

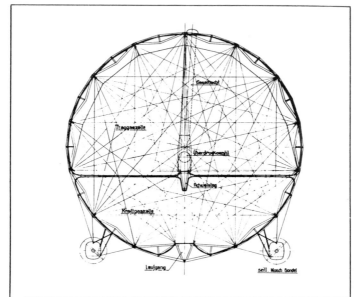

A diagram showing the provision for fuel gas in LZ-127 *Graf Zeppelin*. *von Schiller*

enough to see how the future for civil airships would be imperilled if they were to encounter just one more disaster from such a cause. Eckener kept hoping for supplies of the critically scarce American helium for his civil Zeppelin programmes, but as things stood the most excellent *Graf Zeppelin* still carried only twenty passengers. If ultimately the much-coveted helium were to inflate the *Graf Zeppelin* the loss of payload would virtually eliminate the ability to carry even twenty passengers for more than a very short distance. The options therefore were simple; either you carried on flying with twenty passengers surrounded by hydrogen or you grounded the ship permanently.

The current designs for a bigger ship were therefore scrapped and a new start made on something which, although it would turn out to be vastly bigger in every way, would at least enable a viable passenger load to be carried despite the penalties imposed by helium, always supposing it was available. The R.101 disaster had put Eckener's plans back several years, but lessons had been learned.

Long-term plans for helium-filled ships for the American Navy had been taking a somewhat similar political path to the British plans for the R.100 and R.101, and over a similar period. While ideas had been generated as early as 1924, it was another four years before contracts came to the new Goodyear-Zeppelin Corporation at Akron in Ohio. The requirements were for the development of the rigid airship as a weapons system for the U.S. Navy, the basic airship being intended to function as an aircraft carrier for the fleet and to conduct wide-sweep reconnaissances. One of the first steps in the new programme was the construction at Akron of the world's biggest assembly hall, nearly 1,200 feet long, 200 feet high and more than a hundred yards wide.

The ZRS-4, named *Akron*, began to take shape there soon after the two big British rigids had been launched. It was entirely predictable that *Akron* should exhibit much novelty; it lacked little in the way of development money and with the traditional American flair for building big, coupled with true German expertise, the results were impressive. *Akron* displaced nearly seven million cubic feet, was helium filled and had its engines mounted internally.

Launched in September, 1931, eleven months after the loss of the R.101, the *Akron* took up residence at Lakehurst, New Jersey, just inland from the Atlantic coast and not far from Philadelphia and Washington. As part of the overall scheme, a companion station was very soon opened at Sunnyvale in California on the west coast, thus extending the range of airship operations over the Pacific as well as the Atlantic.

The design finally accepted became the receptacle for numerous innovations

The world's biggest assembly hall, the Goodyear-Zeppelin Corporation at Akron, Ohio, where the two giants *Akron* and *Macron* were built. The clamshell doors are similar to those on some First World War German sheds.
Goodyear

departing from established Zeppelin practices and incorporated many earlier ideas which had been developed to acceptable levels. The many novel features began with the unusual blunt profile of the hull, which contained only twelve gas-cells in place of the usual sixteen to twenty. Instead of a single central keel-corridor, two separate large corridors ran along the sides of the ship, giving access to four separate engine-rooms on either side. Protruding outboard from the engine-rooms were propeller transmission shafts which had swivelling facilities such as had earlier been tried in British wartime rigids. Mounted in multiple panels on the envelope were examples of water recovery units similar to those originally fitted to Britain's *Mayfly* of 1911.

A departure from structural conservatism was the absence of the normal cruciform girder for the support of the tail fins. In the *Akron*, both the horizontal and vertical stabilisers were grafted direct on to the primary structure of the hull itself; a feature that later proved lethal.

Doubtless the most impressive feature of all was the inclusion of a complete aeroplane hangar and an associated trapeze on which single-seat combat aircraft could be launched and retrieved in flight, up to five aeroplanes being carried at a single time.

Akron, with its first flight on 25th September, 1931, subsequently notched up nearly 1,700 flying hours in seventy-three flights. The U.S. Navy's other airship, *Macon*, which first flew on 21st April, 1933, achieved 1,800 flying hours in fifty-four flights.

On 3rd April, 1933, *Akron* set out on a routine training flight with Rear Admiral Moffett on board and ran into freak weather conditions. Unknown to those aboard, they were flying ahead of one of the most violent stormfronts to sweep the North

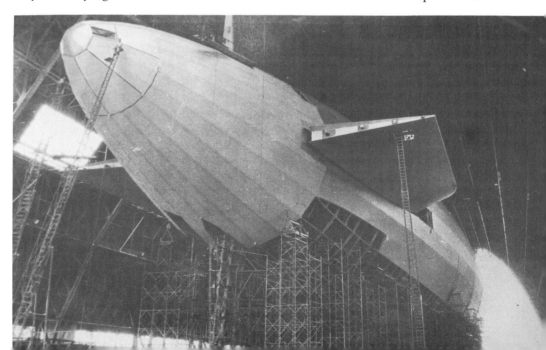

Atlantic states in ten years. Due to a combination of navigational errors and bad radio communication as a result of electrical storms, the ship was caught in the worst part of the storm thirty miles out over the Atlantic.

Trapped by violent temperature inversions producing powerful vertical air currents both upwards and downwards, *Akron* was thrust down into the sea tail first just after midnight, and despite the jettisoning of ballast and the application of full engine power, she survived for only a short while at an acute angle before subsiding into the giant waves caused by the storm. The ship's disintegration was rapid, the loss of life being unnecessarily heavy owing to the absence of life-saving equipment on board. Three out of the total crew of seventy-six survived, they being found clinging to an empty fuel tank.

Macon was lost in the Pacific off the Californian coast on 12th February, 1935. Due to an earlier decision to modify the attachments of the fins to the airframe structure, a protracted series of engineering changes was being embodied. By February all except the upper dorsal fin had been treated, but the modification was one of strengthening and not considered by anyone, least of all the responsible design engineers, to offer any risks to routine flying before the whole of the work had been completed. *Macon* was seen flying only three miles out to sea near Monterey Bay when her uppermost stabiliser fin began to break up.

As the appalled spectators watched, the stern of the airship began sinking steadily towards the sea, the naked stern-post sticking upright and apparently undamaged, with one of the enormous rudders still swinging ineffectively on its hinges. Confusion among the crew, coupled with inaccurate damage reporting to the control centre, resulted in over-reaction, excessive amounts of weight being dropped, and the vessel shot up rapidly to the point where she was well over pressure-height

Opposite: ZRS-4 and ZRS-5, seen here, both lacked the traditional Zeppelin type of cruciform girder stiffening the fins and tailplanes.   *U.S. Navy*

Right: Inside the lower fin of the *Akron*.
                U.S. Navy

and helium was discharged automatically. From that point on, the ship was quite certainly not under control. What had begun as a partial structural failure, in no way critical, escalated into a catastrophic condition where the ship began sinking rapidly, completely out of equilibrium. Nothing the crew could do, including driving the tilting propellers full speed in the lifting mode, could prevent the ultimate splash down.

There are many who, like the Court of Inquiry, believe that this accident to the *Macon* was another of those disasters that need not, and should not, have happened. The saving grace of the calamity was the smaller casualty rate, only two sailors being lost.

Without doubt, it was the end of rigid airship operations with the U.S. Navy, but whether the airship would have prospered anyway is still a moot point.

The end of the American demand for vast quantities of helium encouraged Eckener to hope that his own demands might now be met. His new monster LZ-129 was already in an advanced state of construction and at slightly over seven million cubic feet would need all the helium that America could spare. However, despite the failure of their own airship operations and despite the immense regard they had for Dr Eckener personally, American politicians could never overlook the fact that Germany might again turn the Zeppelin into a significant weapon of war.

When early in 1936 LZ-129 *Hindenburg* came into service refugees from Nazi Germany were already entering the U.S.A. with their evidence of persecution and atrocities. As Eckener showed the world what really could be done with an efficient large civil transport Zeppelin, the tide of international politics turned against him and his last chance of proving the world's finest long-haul passenger transport system was lost.

The story of the dramatic loss of the *Hindenburg* is a familiar one, and the original newsreel of the disaster has been televised throughout the world time after time. But neither the narrative nor the newsreel, nor the film made about the disaster, proved anything any more than all the many speculations about the R.101.

Hindenburg had first flown on 4th March, 1936, and after certification had made fifty-five flights that year totalling 186,420 miles, and had made thirty-four ocean crossings. She had transported 2,800 passengers and had carried 180 tons of mail and assorted cargo, all without accident or injury. The disaster took place on 6th May, 1937, at 6.20 p.m. local time at the end of the *Hindenburg's* first transatlantic voyage of the year, following its annual major overhaul.

As to the cause of the accident, von Schiller was inclined to the theories advanced by Dr Eckener at the Court of Inquiry. Very simply, it began with the occasional transverse bracing wire snapping at one of the main frame positions. *Hindenburg* had been seen to make a tight S-turn shortly before landing and he believed this had over-stressed the bulkhead wiring, causing a broken wire to whiplash with the relieved tension and to slash one or more of the hydrogen-filled cells at the rear.

The ship had already been compelled to delay its landing approach for an appreciable time due to the presence of thunderstorms and heavy rain, and it was technically certain that the ship was strongly charged with static electricity. As the trail ropes were dropped on the approach to the mooring mast they probably earthed the vessel and created an electrical tracking within the structure to ignite the hydrogen escaping from the envelope, just forward of the upper dorsal fin, where the fire was first seen. From that moment, the ship was doomed; the entire gas content burned off in an enormous ball of flame in something like forty-five seconds. Out of ninety-six people aboard, quite incredibly sixty-one survived.

Work continued nevertheless on the LZ-130, first laid down in June, 1936, and on 14th September, 1938, it made its first flight under the command of Dr Eckener, who christened it *Graf Zeppelin*, despite the original *Graf* still being in flying condition. According to von Schiller, some thirty-odd experimental flights were

The new *Graf Zeppelin* of 1938.
Royal Aeronautical Society

made. The LZ-130 was virtually a replica of *Hindenburg*, except that the propellers were mounted as tractors instead of pushers so as to make room for some water-recovery apparatus for the ballast system.

That last year of peace before the Second World War saw the flying of the two *Graf Zeppelin* airships around Europe in charge of the Luftwaffe. After Dr Eckener had supervised the first few flights, LZ-130 was handed over to Hans von Schiller, backed up by Anton Witteman and Albert Sammt. Both ships were still flying with hydrogen, the only helium source still being completely American.

The military used these ships in the summer of 1939 to spy on the frontiers with Russia and France. They also set out to verify whether reports from Luft Hansa aircrews respecting towers seen along the British east coast, believed to have been for the earliest radar installations, were true.* That the suspicions of the Germans were well founded is now a matter of history, but ironically the assessments made by scientists flying in the airships proved to be Germany's undoing. It was the failure of the Zeppelin's detection equipment to identify radar signals that led to Goering's fatal assumption that Britain was at a similar stage to Germany, whose experiments had not progressed very far.

*See *Bawdsey — Birth of the Beam*, by Gordon Kinsey, published by Terence Dalton, 1983.

It was not until 1982 that the detailed truth became fully public when Wolfgang von Zeppelin produced a biography of Albert Sammt very shortly before the latter's death on 21st June at the age of 93. Sammt had commanded the LZ-130 on these reconnaissance flights and had given a first-hand account.

Having originally been a member of aircrew on the 1912 civil Zeppelins, Albert Sammt became a Zeppelin engineer at Potsdam and Staaken during the First World War. He stayed on with the Zeppelin company to become an experienced helmsman during the 1920's. Like his contemporary Max Prüss, he went on by stages to become first a navigator and then a watch officer. He was acting in this capacity on the

Max Prüss, left, and Albert Sammt in the *Hindenburg* in 1937.

von Zeppelin

Hindenburg when that ship crashed in America, and with Prüss, who was in command, survived his injuries to be able to perform actively on *Hindenburg's* successor, LZ-130.

It is evident that these spy flights of LZ-130 went on at intervals right up to a month before the outbreak of war. Sammt captained the ship, which contained twenty-four V.H.F. and U.H.F. detector installations, the sensor antennae of which were controlled by an operator in a nacelle suspended below the hull of the airship on a cable of considerable length. The entire installation was in the direct charge of Ernst Breuning, a young qualified electronics engineer. Dr Breuning, still a breezy young seventy, tells a fascinating story of the forty-eight-hour flight of the LZ-130 on its cruise round Britain at the beginning of August, 1939. Simulating an engine difficulty, the ship drifted over sensitive R.A.F. bases in Scotland, finally being warned off by a horde of attentive Spitfires whose pilots were doubtless itching to put a few rounds into her!

The Zeppelins, which had lost their offensive in the First World War, were blamed also for losing Goering's initiative in the Battle of Britain. On 6th May, 1940, the anniversary of the loss of the *Hindenburg*, both *Graf Zeppelins* were destroyed and their Frankfurt hangar blown up.

CHAPTER THIRTEEN

Epilogue

A T FIRST sight, little seems to have changed at the Cardington Royal Aircraft Establishment since the heyday of the giant rigids. Turning in at the main gates on top of the hill, one immediately encounters the old familiar green wooden shack with its notice board over the door proclaiming it still to be the "Shortstown Post Office". Not many yards away, just about where another much larger notice board once declared the establishment to be the "Royal Airship Works", there now stands a newer signboard which reveals that this Ministry of Defence establishment is the home of "No. 217 Maintenance Unit, Royal Air Force".

The multi-storey administration block is a massive red brick structure in the original Admiralty style, about a hundred yards in length and set back from the main road by some thirty yards, the centre point in between being occupied by an imposing flagstaff bearing the Royal Air Force ensign. Externally, the only major visible change is the absence of the control tower and its tall wireless mast. Added to the building in 1928 for the ill-fated civil airship programme, it survived till as recently as 1983 when it had become unsafe and was condemned. The rest of this historic building remains foursquare and intact, the builder's inscription over the portico with its original revolving doors clearly reading "MCMXVII" (the year 1917 being the date of completion).

Behind this great edifice, a spread of several acres retains the original airship manufacturing workshops, again basically unchanged and when last visited in 1983 still utilising a considerable area for the maintenance and repair of balloon envelopes needed for meteorological work and for the training of paratroops. A certain amount of space clearing has been carried out on the south side of the complex in the area once devoted to the production of hydrogen, from which point it used to be piped underground to the hangars and to the mooring mast through a mile or so of 18 inch diameter main. Looking south across the airfield from the brow of Shortstown hill, a scatter of small new trees has appeared, together with a few odd army huts here and there. The two enormous airship sheds, however, dominate the entire landscape and are still the greatest buildings of their kind anywhere outside of America, and certainly are of greater age than those which do still survive on the other side of the Atlantic.

The only really significant change in the Cardington scene is the absence of the great steel mooring tower. Erected in 1926 for the civil programme, it stood unused until the Second World War when it was dismantled for scrap. Seventy feet in diameter at the base and two hundred and two feet in height, the tower was the first ever cantilever mooring mast to have been built. Forty years after the demolition of the mast, its jagged stumps are still to be found protruding through its original concrete base, while its one-time power house still stands, serving to house a local farmer's tractors. As late as 1983, one could still gaze meditatively at the large collapsed pile of a clapboard building which had once performed the historic role of Customs Office for passengers travelling abroad by airship. It was used as such on three occasions; twice in respect of the R.100's out and return flight to Canada and once on that fateful day of 4th October, 1930, for the R.101.

So far as the hangars are concerned, there seems no good reason why these should ever be dismantled. They have served many valuable purposes over the ensuing years and are now officially listed as historic buildings.

The two sheds lie parallel to one another on an east to west line. The northerly shed, known as "No. 1 Shed", was the site for the erection of the R.101, while "No. 2 Shed" was reserved for the accommodation of R.100; it was here that this airship was dismantled. Approaching it in modern times, one is struck by the complete absence of glass in its many window frames, due to the fact that for a considerable period it has been occupied by the Fire Research Unit of the Building Research Institute, itself a division of the Department of the Environment. The D.O.E. has a number of different sections operating at the establishment and this particular one

The Cardington control tower, erected in 1928, with its radio mast above.
R.A.E. Cardington
Crown copyright

The Cardington mooring mast was sacrificed to the war effort in 1943. Here the Station C.O. ceremonially severs one of the legs with a cutting torch.   *R.A.E. Cardington, Crown copyright*

makes very good use of the unique character of this building. Here, under cover, houses can be built; by starting controlled fires technicians carry out valuable testing of fire-alarm systems and fire resistant materials and investigation of the ways in which fires spread.

Ever since 1947, the Department of the Environment, under varying names, has had many units based at Cardington, the largest of which is the D.O.E. Training Centre. This caters for a vast selection of courses attended by over 14,000 students annually in well-equipped lecture rooms and laboratories suited to most of the technological disciplines.

Discoveries of this sort tend to be a trifle disconcerting to visiting air enthusiasts, but their qualms are soon alleviated on entering No. 1 Hangar, where work is usually to be found in progress on lighter-than-air projects of one kind or another. It has been common experience to enter this vast cavern and to find it almost completely occupied by the most fascinating collection of gas-balloons of all shapes and sizes. Such balloons are quite frequently put to work and flown within this 200-feet high shed before being taken outside for more serious testing. A multitude of balloon types have been developed at Cardington over a lengthy period and for a great variety of applications. They have carried measuring instruments for the assessment of weather conditions, air pollution and magnetic disturbances. Occasionally they

189

have been adapted quite simply to the uplifting of aerial cameras and even special television antennae. For very many years this has been the scene of constant experimental work with gas balloons, but some high-altitude instrumentation studies are now being undertaken with satellite aids and so the range of work at Cardington can be seen to be diminishing.

One most surprising spin-off from Cardington's expertise in balloons has been the fashioning of endless varieties of inflatable products, utilising proofed fabrics developed initially for balloon work but found to be infinitely adaptable. Although Cardington originally perfected this technique for military purposes in the form of dummy tanks and aeroplanes, etc., these skills have since extended far beyond such obvious applications. Much genuine originality stems from Cardington's direct involvement in the development of airborne dinghies, lifeboats, lifejackets, hover-

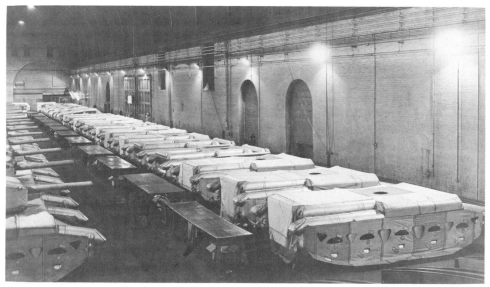

Cardington-made dummy tanks designed to mislead German aerial reconnaissance in the days leading up to the invasion of Europe. *R.A.E. Cardington, Crown copyright*

craft, inflatable wing aeroplanes, immersion suits, inflatable hangars and so on, until Cardington's native ingenuity seems inexhaustible.

As is apparent from almost any photograph of the hangars, a sloping annexe extends the full length of each side of both buildings, providing office and workshop areas without impeding the clear space of the main hangar floor. Most of the available space in the lean-to area on the south side of No. 1 shed is occupied not by offices but by many large crates covered by heavily dust-coated tarpaulins, most of them dating back to the pre-war period 1933 to 1938 when No. 2 Aircraft Storage Unit (R.A.F.) had the care of great quantities of obsolete aircraft and ancillary equipment. There was a time when the hangar seemed to be almost filled with surplus aeroplanes and many others were parked in rows on the grass outside. Visions remain of acres of sad-looking Avros, Tomtits, Bulldogs and twin-engined Vickers Virginias.

Nowadays only the crates remain, and it is from these Pandora's Boxes that magic continues to be extracted and refurbished before appearing at the Royal Air Force Museum, Hendon.

On that same patch of ground outside No. 1 shed there now exists a great compound of stored gas-cylinders, stockholdings of which were at one time in excess of one hundred thousand. Virtually all of the three armed services' requirements for industrial gases and associated devices were catered for from here for many years. Before the Beeching cuts took away the Bedford to Hitchin railway line, most of Cardington's heavy and bulky supplies came right through to this point on sidings put down when the station was originally built. All the establishment's transport needs have now to be met by road vehicles, but historians will be glad to know that two original brick-built loco sheds still stand adjacent to the big glass-roofed building known affectionately even today as "the Arcade".

This is largest of all the buildings at Cardington, other than the hangars themselves, and it was here under carefully controlled conditions of humidity, temperature and cleanliness that all the major gas-cell work was carried out from the very beginning of Cardington's airship years. A similar smaller adjacent building still carries on with the work of maintenance and repair of gas-balloon envelopes, but in "the Arcade" something different is afoot. Over the past decade this area has become a workshop and stores annexe to the R.A.F. Museum, and here a small team of dedicated specialists laboured long and hard under the supervision and inspired

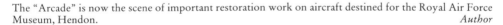

The "Arcade" is now the scene of important restoration work on aircraft destined for the Royal Air Force Museum, Hendon.   *Author*

leadership of the now retired W. H. Sayers. Undoubtedly the controlled environment of "the Arcade" is a great asset in the restoration of rotting, broken and obsolete aeroplanes and equipment, which occasionally must appear to be beyond redemption. It occasions no surprise to discover that the indefatigable Bill Sayers now takes on the responsiblity for monitoring the airworthiness of "those Magnificent Flying Machines" of the Shuttleworth Trust at Old Warden, just south of Cardington.

Crossing the few yards that separate the workshops from the main office block, we enter the reception hall of the main building and immediately are made aware of its historic airship origins. This lofty space, some forty feet square, has corridors branching away from it on either side, leading to the offices once occupied by doyens of the airship world such as Richmond, Scott, Colmore, Irwin and Booth. About one-eighth part of the floor space is taken up by a glass showcase in which a giant model of the R.101 poses majestically at a model tower. Numerous small relics of the airship days repose in smaller display cabinets around the hall, while one side wall is adorned with the helm from the R.100 and the opposite wall gives prominence to the master girder joint from the same ship, demonstrating at a glance the brilliant simplicity of its design, created by Sir Barnes Wallis.

During a visit to this place in 1980, the writer entered the first office of the south wing of the building, armed with the knowledge that this had at one time been Colonel Richmond's sanctum. Its present occupier was the Station C.O., Wing Commander A. R. Murray. It was sobering to recall that from this very room Colonel Richmond had written to Sir John Higgins after the first few flights of the R.101 to emphasise to him that the two new ships would be too small to be able to carry a hundred passengers to India with regularity. Clearly Richmond was already feeling apprehensive of the future, and he reinforced that outlook by his submission that nothing smaller than a ship of nine million cubic feet would suffice. It is on record that within two months of that communication Richmond was already planning the R.102 of 8.3 million cubic feet, driven by gas engines, inspired no doubt by the successful German experiments with the *Graf Zeppelin*.

It would be difficult today to say to what extent the gloom and depression in that office block leaked out, but as the months passed until the India flight could no longer be put off, tension had certainly reached many of the crewmen. Even Commander Atherstone put pen to paper on the day before the fateful flight began: "There are so many unknown factors that a thing called 'Luck' will figure rather conspicuously in our flight. Let us hope for good luck and do our best."

After the disaster it was generally conceded that this was the grand finale for British airships, but the day to day activities of Cardington continued for quite a while as the future of the establishment hung in the balance. There was, of course, the immediate requirement to get investigation and work teams organised and sent out to Beauvais. The first such expedition was led by the Chief Inspector of Accidents, Major J. P. C. Cooper from the Air Ministry, accompanied by Professor L.

Above: The final state of applying the "goldbeater's skin" to the insides of gascells at Cardington. Two and sometimes three layers would be applied with rubber solution to the cotton cell and then varnish-brushed to minimise hydrogen leakage. *H. G. Parker*

Right: The date of Cardington's origins. *Author*

Below: Cleansing animal intestines for the making of "goldbeater's skin" at Cardington about 1918. *H. G. Parker*

Bairstow, of the Government's Airship Advisory Panel. Also in the party were Squadron Leader Booth (Captain of the R.100), Mr T. S. D. Collins (Cardington Stress Office), Mr R. Gerrish (Cardington General Manager), Mr R. Randle (Cardington Drawing Office), and Mr F. McWade (A.I.D.). These seven were immediately formed into an on-site investigation committee chaired by Air Commodore Holt and further supported by two French delegates. Afterwards another team went out to retrieve wreckage samples and certain strategic components. The engines, for example, were cut out, crated and returned to Cardington for intensive examination and testing. One such engine remains in London's Science Museum, though efforts to identify it as one of those from the crash have not been successful. Certainly there did exist a number of spare engines which were held in stock at Cardington and in Egypt and India.

Apart from detailed investigation research on behalf of the Inquiry Committee, work continued at Cardington on a care and maintenance basis on R.100, now sorely in need of a new envelope and a number of technical modifications. Monies had not been forthcoming, but as yet hopes were far from being extinguished. Most things remained in a state of suspension awaiting the publication of the full R.101 Accident Report and its subsequent debate. This came in the spring of 1931 as the great Depression of the thirties began to bite.

As Cardington kept hoping for a continuation and even an extension of its work, it became steadily more evident that it was not to be. Sir Richard Wells, the local Conservative M.P., worked hard to keep the topic to the fore in the Commons. Ultimately, this and other considerations did lead to a vote of half a million sterling

The R.100 being dismantled at Cardington in May, 1931.   *R.A.E. Cardington, Crown copyright*

(at 1930 values this would equate to some £20 million in 1983) being approved by the Prime Minister, Ramsey MacDonald. To the eventual bitterness of Bedfordians in particular and airship enthusiasts in general, the Committee on National Expenditure effectively killed off any further hopes of an airship revival.

That was in May, 1931. From that time on, Cardington had its work cut out to survive, and although fundamentally it has had to turn its back on its prodigious airship origins it has since given this country very good value for money in all the many services it has been able to perform. Initially the closure of the station was almost total, with most of the permanent staff being re-appointed to R.A.E., Farnborough. At its lowest ebb, the staff dwindled to forty-four, about the smallest number that could effectively prevent the establishment from becoming derelict. That included the housing estate of about sixty dwellings, half of which were soon unoccupied. During this distressing period, T. S. D. Collins became Station Superintendent; Rogers, the one-time gas plant engineer, became Clerk of Works, while Warren took on the task of Estate Foreman.

The death knell of British rigids came with the arrival of outside contractors who carted away for scrap the bare bones of the R.100, dismantled by the very men who had previously flown her with great pride. One can only guess at the turmoil of emotions suffered by men placed in this unenviable situation.

Work at Cardington took on a more serious note once it was evident that our industrial cities would be vulnerable targets for Germany's new bombers. As a contribution to their defence it had been decided to resurrect that feature of London's First World War defence system known as the Balloon Barrage (or an improved version of it). The major snag was the vast scale of the logistics, involving some thousands of large kite balloons, needed for giving protection to the multitude of places requiring the system. Enormous quantities of high-grade rubberised fabrics had to be made, and much labour and skill would go into making the balloons. The balloons would have to be large enough to lift a couple of miles of steel cable, tethered to a motorised winch. Every balloon and winch required mobile transport, as well as crews trained to a high level of competence and able to provide monitoring attention twenty-four hours a day throughout the year and in all weathers. Every site would require its own store of hydrogen cylinders and in many instances a fair-sized hangar for repair and maintenance work. Thanks to an early start being made on the problem at Cardington, this aspect of the country's defence programme was thoroughly implemented.

Preparations for meeting this demand began in November, 1936, when the station first became known as Royal Air Force Station, Cardington and Group Captain A. A. Thomson, M.C., A.F.C., became its first commanding officer. Initially the task of the Unit was to train barrage balloon crews, but basic training of recruits for the R.A.F. also began early the following year. As for the existing Royal Airship Works, it had already begun an extensive programme of balloon research and development under its new Design Chief, Mr C. Durston, previously of the R.101

195

A typical Cardington balloon of the kind used both in the balloon barrage of the Second World War and for parachute training.

R.A.E. Cardington, Crown copyright

Drawing Office Staff. Gerry Long, one-time cox'n of the R.100, headed the hangar and workshop team, which included others of the R.100 crew such as Moncrieff, Hobbs, Mann and Deverell, together with the R.101 survivors, Binks and Bell. They were joined by Armstrong, Norman and Westgate from Pulham.

"Jock" Armstrong, incidentally, was a frequent visitor to Cardington until his death early in 1983, and even Sewell Norman, now in his nineties, cannot seem to stay away from the place. The resources of the fabric shop were very limited at the time and such early experimental work as was needed was done by four ladies with the names of Clarke, Moore, Mann and Jeeves.

Eventually, in 1938, the once proud title of Royal Airship Works was surrendered and The Balloon Development Establishment took its place. As war became imminent, training work at Cardington moved into top gear. By September, 1939, when war began, not only was the output of trained operators exceeding anything previously imagined but, of equal significance, the manufacturing resources of Cardington's one-time airship works were pouring out completed balloons at a fantastic rate. At its peak, Cardington was producing twenty-six balloons a week. Simultaneously, personnel from outside industries were being trained at Cardington before returning to their employers to set up similar production lines. By the end of 1943 all these requirements had been met, and when No.1 Balloon Training Unit finally closed some 10,000 operators and a further 12,000 operator/drivers had been trained.

Nowadays it is quite common to encounter friends who recall their first brief period of service in the R.A.F. at Cardington, but usually such people had no opportunity to discover the history of Cardington, neither did they comprehend the scale of the exercise of which they formed an infinitesimal part. It should intrigue readers to learn that about a quarter million recruits actually joined the R.A.F. at Cardington. Many thousands were also demobilised there through No. 102 Personnel Despatch Centre, set up in May, 1945.

One division of the Cardington Balloon Establishment known as "The Balloon Unit" moved out and was resettled at Hullavington in Wiltshire as recently as 1966. The Balloon Establishment had already in 1945 lost its definitive identity when it became the Ministry of Supply Research and Development Establishment. The same unit is still there, having served a consistent role under the control of successive government departments such as the Ministry of Technology and later the Ministry of Defence (Procurement Executive).

Almost as we go to press, it has been reported unofficially that all balloon work will finish at Cardington in the mid-summer of 1984 and that such work will be carried on as and when needed by outside contracting companies.

The transition of peacetime operations brought about the return to London's bigger museums of many valuable artifacts held at Cardington for safe-keeping during the war. Another event was the move to Cardington in 1948 of No.279 Maintenance Unit under the command initially of Squadron-Leader J. A. Colvin. The unit was made responsible for the production, storage and distribution of compressed gases, besides maintaining and repairing all the gas cylinders used by the British armed services throughout the world. When the famous French balloonist Dr Dollfus came to Britain at the invitation of the Royal Aeronautical Society, in May, 1949, the staff at Cardington gave him all the assistance and gas supplies he needed to perform at the society's prestigious Garden Party at White Waltham. A similar service was provided when another ascent was made from The Duke of York's Headquarters in Sloane Square, in aid of Chelsea Charity Week.

A similar unit to No.279 M.U. was later set up at Wellingborough, but by 1955 the two separate units had combined to become No.217 M.U. at Cardington. As such, the unit has continued this function in a modified form to the present day, and since 1967 has been the commanding unit of R.A.F. Cardington.

Although Cardington has undergone many changes in its official role, there has always remained a certain indefinable aura about the place which has captured the imagination of people with visions of a return to airship flight, however elementary and modest. The first of these revivalists was, predictably, the noted Lord Ventry, Britain's most celebrated airship crusader and editor of a private journal on airships over many years. Lord Ventry had himself served in the R.A.F. during both wars, in the first of which he was involved with airships both at Howden and Pulham. It was in the second war when he was at Cardington that he found himself flying in a French balloon of unusual shape. He realised immediately that it could easily be converted into a small power-driven airship.

The idea never left him, and in 1948 he gathered around him a few of his old airship friends and together they formed a small fund-raising society which they called The Airship Club (the author was a member) with the object of creating the first airship to be made in Britain for twenty years. Some additional help was given by the Corporation of Bournemouth where Lord Ventry lived, and in return the future airship was to carry the name of *Bournemouth* on its envelope. His immediate assistants were Squadron-Leader York Moore, George Manning, Freddy Twinn, Eric Eveleigh Smith, M. Cromey Hawk and Alec Leith, all of whom had acquired experience with non-rigids during the first war.

A surplus envelope of the type originally envisaged was purchased from the Air Ministry and taken to the R.F.D. company at Guildford, where its length of 92 feet was increased to 108 feet. The diameter of 28 feet remained unaltered and this provided a gross volume of 45,000 cubic feet. With a maximum inflation of commercial hydrogen, this would have lifted about 3,000 lb, but to be able to control the envelope's expansion and contraction in flight, two large air bags called ballonets were fitted within the interior and had a maximum inflation capacity of 5,000 cubic feet. This is normal practice in non-rigid airships (sometimes called pressure ships), because an internal pressure is vital for maintaining both the shape and the

The modified *Bournemouth* at her mobile mooring mast in 1952.　　　　　*Lord Ventry*

near-rigidity of the hull when internal gas pressures are affected by altitude and environmental changes. Manual control of the ballonet pressures and volumes can also be applied in flight to obtain control of the vessel in the pitch axis.

Under the watchful eye of Lord Ventry, Alec Leith designed and built a control car 15 feet long by 4 feet wide. Assembled at Hurn airport, it was fitted with a French radial engine of 60 h.p. at the rear end, driving a four-bladed wooden propeller. The control surfaces were also made at Hurn and in the spring of 1951 all the components were taken to Cardington for erection in No.2 hangar. The Cardington airship professionals could hardly wait to get their hands on it and L. A. Speed, late of the R.101 drawing office, was quick to design the vital suspension and attachment of the car to the envelope. Help of many kinds came from Flight-Lieutenant A. Richardson, a possessor of airship experience from the First World War. The erection of the new midget was undertaken mainly by two R.100 men, Gerry Long and Ralph Deverell, and the R.101 survivors Arthur Bell and Joe Binks.

Leaking gas valves delayed the inflation tests but eventually the lift and trim trials began in July, 1951, and these proved a capacity to uplift four crew, plus 260 lbs of ballast and twelve gallons of petrol, sufficient for three hours. In the fore part of the car separate helm wheels controlled rudders and elevators, while behind that was space for two passengers, and at the rear room for the flight engineer. Protruding below the envelope was a light metal air scoop, made to hinge downwards into the propeller slipstream for inflating the ballonets. On either side of the ship was the name *Bournemouth* and the town's crest, while the registration G-AMJH appeared on the fin.

A first test-flight of twenty-five minutes was made on 19th July by Captain Jack Beckford Ball, a newcomer with experience of having piloted a similar small ship, the AD-1, built and flown at Newcastle in 1929. Twinn, Bell and Richardson were also on board during this maiden flight, a safe one but one which revealed that *Bournemouth* was very nose heavy and her controls were almost ineffective. Another flight was made on 28th July but a forced landing was made after twenty minutes when rudder cables came adrift. Main-road traffic had to be held up while the airship was walked back across the road to its hangar. Apart from the rudder failure, trim was now too far aft. More changes took place before the third flight on 17th August when Lord Ventry himself joined the crew, but again bad luck dogged the event, more seriously this time. There was an improvement in fore and aft control but the rudders could not hold the incessant yawing of the nose. Flying back, the ship passed too low over some army huts and her trail ropes fouled an obstruction which brought her down hard on a roof, smashing windows and tearing the envelope. The propeller broke up but remarkably nobody was hurt.

It was a full year before repair work was completed, aided this time by E. J. Mann, in charge of the de Havilland Apprentices' School at Hatfield. Here, he redesigned and rebuilt the control surfaces, which were a great success on the next trials on 8th September, 1952. Meanwhile an old single-decker omnibus had been acquired and fitted with a stub mast, enabling the now rebuilt ship to be towed out of the hangar, well under control. Two good flights were made that day, one of forty minutes and one of twenty minutes. Ten days later, after further adjustments, two more flights were made in one day.

As part of the 1952 Battle of Britain celebrations, *Bournemouth* flew over Bedford for 1 hour 55 minutes, her longest flight and her last. She was deflated and stowed away for the winter while plans went ahead for improvements based on the experience obtained from her eight flights totalling six and a half flying hours. *Bournemouth's* end came on 24th April, 1953, in No.2 Hangar when some netting slipped. The envelope tore badly and the front portion reared up into the roof as the rear part collapsed on the floor. This and other damage made further repair work impractical and so the unfortunate ship never did fly over Bournemouth.

Nothing more in the airship world took place to affect Cardington until 1970, when the Goodyear Tire & Rubber Company of Akron, Ohio, which had many years earlier formed an alliance with the Zeppelin Company to built giant rigid airships for the U.S. Navy, brought to England one of its small airships or "blimps", as they were known in America. Between 1911 and 1978, Goodyear produced an astonishing total of 287 airships, including the two monsters *Akron* and *Macon*. Millions of Americans had become accustomed to the sight of the tubby little Goodyear "blimps", particularly at night when huge electric flashing signs were displayed on both sides of their envelopes. These ships, just under 200 feet long and some 200,000 cubic feet in capacity, are the successors to the many Service ships built during the Second World War when they gave escort to nearly 100,000 shipping sorties without loss of a single surface ship, much as their British counterparts had done in the First World War.

Goodyear's post-war commercial airships were a mix of refurbished ex-Navy ships and a few brand-new specimens with improved styling. Names chosen for these ships displayed the American flair for emotional appeal such as *Mayflower, Venture, Ranger, Enterprise, Puritan, Columbia, America* and so on. It soon became clear that these operations had become a permanent part of American life, with three ships operating regularly out of permanent bases at Miami, Houston, and Los Angeles. This so impressed Mr T. J. Allison, Director of Special Projects for the Goodyear Public Relations Department, that he began to look towards Europe for an extension of this attractive and very successful policy.

By the end of 1970, an identical project was set up for the European scene, the name for the ship *Europa*. Construction began in the following January, while in February selections were made from the existing crews to provide a nucleus crew for *Europa*. All work of this kind was done by Henry H. Nettling, Manager of Airship Operations. Simultaneously, a team of European tehnicians was recruited and sent to America for instruction in the handling and maintenance of the new ship in service.

On 10th December, 1971, everything was loaded on to the "Guppy" aeroplane N.1037V at Akron and flown from there direct to R.A.E. Bedford, the one-time wartime home of the U.S.A.A.F. Here, five miles north of Bedford, the load was taken by road to Cardington for erection in the No.1 hangar. *Europa's* very first flight was made from Cardington on 8th March, 1972, with Mr R. W. Widdicombe as pilot in charge. His immediate deputy was John Moran. Both men were, of course, American.

There followed a period of flight proving trials which were almost completed in April when calamity struck *Europa*. A gale in the night tore her from her moorings and the unmanned airship bounded across the countryside in a series of giant leaps until the obstructions of the nearby village of Cotton End blocked her further progress. *Europa* was impaled on a tree in the grounds of Manor Farm, once the home of the late Major Scott of the much lamented R.101.

It was 25th June before repairs were completed and *Europa* was able to carry out three days of trials to gain her American airworthiness certificate. She was immediately put into operational service under the direction of "Dick" Widdicombe, aided by John Moran and Tom Gilmer, Chief Engineer. The first full team put into the field by Goodyear to operate *Europa* numbered twenty, of whom four were Italian, two Dutch and the remainder American.

The Goodyear *Europa* being launched on 8th March, 1972, with one of the Cardington sheds in the background.
Goodyear

Anthony Smith at the controls of the *Santos Dumont*.   *Mike Wells*

These men had been training in Akron while a dozen other Americans had been assembling *Europa* at Cardington under the supervision of Mr J. Prinzo, Jack la Fountaine, Arthur Kiel and John Pascu. In the mere two days that *Europa* first operated publicly, her debut could not have been more successful. On 28th June twelve flights were made, carrying a total of sixty-seven passengers, and on the following day, a further 111 passengers flew around Bedford in *Europa*, including those two celebrities Lord Ventry and Arthur Bell.

All told, it was a very good start. Next day, *Europa* flew off to take up residence at Leavesden, just outside Watford. Here for the next three weeks everyone settled into the new routine of giving flights around the locality to a variety of V.I.P.s.

On 20th July, 1972, *Europa* left Britain via Customs at Ashford in Kent and flew to Calais to begin her belated tour of Europe where she would be able to use her electric night displays, which until 1983 were illegal in Britain.

Europa has a gross lift of about 12,000 lb and a Useful Lift of about a quarter of that amount, adequate for some 500 miles at 40 m.p.h. with pilot and six passengers. Two air-cooled engines of 210 h.p. each drive pusher propellers.

By 1980 *Europa* had flown over 14,500 hours and had carried more than 66,000 passengers, plus many television cameramen and technicians filming events like Wimbledon, motor racing at Brands Hatch and the Wembley Cup Final. This ship has ranged from Athens in the south to Stockholm in the north, most big cities in fourteen different countries being visited.

Every time *Europa* returns to Britain it is a reminder of Cardington's further contribution to airship history. A pleasing spin-off is the stimulus given to others to follow suit, even at an amateur level, as with the earlier *Bournemouth* project. In 1974–75, the B.B.C. produced an entrancing documentary film of the construction and flying of a home-made airship, appropriately called *Santos Dumont*; that was the name of the little Franco-Brazilian who had such enormous fun with a tiny single-seat airship in Paris around 1910. Its modern counterpart was filmed on location in its natural environment of Cardington with its creator, Anthony Smith, founder in 1965 of the British Balloon and Airship Club. *Santos Dumont* lay for some years in the darker recesses of Cardington, but has since been moved to Bristol, where, hopefully, it may again take to the air.

As Anthony Smith had prophesied, the airship revival had begun. The stirrings of a new and more serious project had begun to excite another young Englishman, Roger Munk, a professional naval architect. From his studies of airship technology, Munk became painfully aware that much had changed since airships had last been flown commercially half a century ago. Modern materials, components and processes had come a very long way since then. As early as 1971 Munk had gathered together his original small team of engineers and physicists to begin their investigations, and in the following three years they carried out feasibility studies on behalf of one of the big oil companies, who were contemplating long-haul transport of natural gas in bulk at low pressures. This project was basically non-productive but it led to the formation of Munk's first company, Aerospace Developments Ltd., and to the design of his first airship to be built, the *AD-500*.

The first visible evidence of work in progress was seen by the general public in April, 1977, when Munk displayed his one-piece mould for the fibreglass control car at Cardington's open day in No.1 Hangar. For quite some time, nothing much else was to be found there other than the new cluster of portakabins, their bearded occupants wandering around with rolls of drawings tucked under their leather-patched elbows. Subsequent visits, however, revealed the arrival of sundry crates containing things like engines and propellers. The newest technologies were employed. For the envelope the old well-established balloon makers of Paris, Aerazur Zodiac, supplied Munk with a near leak-proof assembly using Dacron high tensile composite fabrics. Vickers Slingsby in Yorkshire produced a remarkable one-piece control car moulded in Kevlar, a new fibreglass material which is fireproof and has five times the strength of an equivalent weight of steel. The floors and bulkheads are of a honeycomb sandwich construction, made from a fire-resistant aramid paper faced with fibreglass. Similar materials are used for the large aerofoil surfaces made by Ciba-Geigy of Cambridge.

Under the rear floor of the gondola are two flat-six aircooled piston engines from Porsche of Germany. These lie on either side of the centre line and deliver some 200 h.p. each through Westland helicopter shafts to separate five-bladed, variable pitch outboard propellers housed in long-chord fibreglass ducts. The ducts protect ground personnel from injury from the propellers; reduce the cabin noise level; and raise propeller efficiency. A principal design feature, revived from Britain's first rigid airships, is the capacity to rotate the complete propeller and duct assemblies at the extremities of their drive shafts. The principal advantage of this is to reduce the dependence on a large ground-handling party, whether for take-off or for landing.

In flight, the *AD-500* looks very similar to the *Europa*, but at 164 feet length it is in fact 28 feet shorter and also some 21,000 cubic feet less in volume. Despite its being appreciably smaller than *Europa*, the new design reflects the advances achieved with modern materials by having a greater disposable lift and a higher maximum speed. So positive is the all-round improvement in performance that the further development into 1984 of the newest model, *Skyship 600*, which approximates more closely to the size of *Europa*, has given some quite startling figures.

The one-piece plastic moulding for the control-car of *AD-500*.   *Author*

The *Skyship 600* is designed to have a Useful Lift of 6,250 pounds, as against the 3,280 pounds of *Europa*; likewise the maximum design speed is 75 m.p.h., which shows a big increase on the 50 m.p.h. actually published by Goodyear for the *Europa*.

Such results have not been obtained easily or quickly. It was fully eight years from the time when Roger Munk's team first got together that the prototype *AD-500* first flew at Cardington in the spring of 1979. Even then, the older local residents took to wagging their heads sadly as the legendary Cardington jinx cast its shadow over the newest residents of No.1 Hangar. After only two short local flights, *AD-500* (registered G-BECE), became a total write-off after being severely damaged by gale-force winds at her stub mooring mast.

Another two years were to elapse before a replacement appeared, in the shape of G-BIHN, now known as *Skyship 500*. Apart from some minor detail changes it was identical to the original *AD-500*. The first few flights of the new ship at the end of September, 1981, were blessed with possibly the finest flying weather of the whole year. A further delight for the author was a renewed meeting with Peter Buckley, the new Chief Operations Pilot, who was assisting Commander "Nick" Bennett, the Chief Test Pilot. I had last met Peter Buckley in June, 1979, when he gave me the controls of *Europa* on a flight from Greenham Common to Fairoaks in Surrey. During his years of flying for Goodyear, Peter Buckley had built up some 5,000 hours of airship flying time, a massive experience now at the disposal of Airship Industries, his new employer.

In the summer of 1983 that experience was put to good use when he was posted to Toronto to supervise an exciting new project. All the components for a new *Skyship 500* were shipped out to Canada, where the company's engineers assembled the first airship of what it is hoped will be a continuous stream of overseas projects. On 19th June, 1983, Buckley took off from Toronto and, crossing Lake Ontario, flew by stages through New York State and New Jersey to Virginia and North Carolina. Several hundreds of hours of flight trials and demonstrations were carried out during the latter months of 1983, principally for the benefit of the U.S. Navy and U.S. Coastguard. By that time a second kit of parts had arrived in Toronto and a back-up ship was being prepared for further sales demonstrations in North America. Numerous potential customers in South America having also shown positive interest, the prospects of meeting a very wide variety of customer needs in foreign countries seems almost assured.

Back in the U.K., technical proving trials and evaluation trials had logged a total of some 800 flying hours by the end of 1983. *Skyship* had been flown both at the

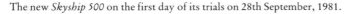

The new *Skyship 500* on the first day of its trials on 28th September, 1981.   *Author*

The maiden flight of of the *Skyship-600* from Cardington on 6th March, 1984.   *Airship Industries*

Farnborough and Paris Air Shows and successful shuttle flights between the two major Paris airports had been conducted under all weather conditions for a fortnight. On 15th November, official mid-stage certification had been granted by the C.A.A. in the Transport Category and a final full Certificate of Airworthiness for the carriage of passengers for hire or reward was being sought in the very near future.

However tempting it might be at this stage to forecast what that future might hold, it is desirable instead to backtrack some five years to record a rather curious and confusing set of commercial circumstances that produced a backcloth to these events. It is difficult to describe those circumstances with accuracy, but nonetheless they must not be ignored.

In 1978 three embryo airship manufacturers merged to form the group known as Airship Industries Ltd., with offices in London, Cardington and the Isle of Man. The extent to which the aims, the facilities and the resources of the three companies are pooled has never been made clear, nor has it even been stated whether pooling of resources really was intended. Roger Munk's prototype bore the name "Aerospace

Developments", while the signwriting on the later ships read "Airship Industries". Almost from the beginning Roger Munk has publicised a comprehensive range of non-rigid airships, to be evolved on a clearly orthodox line of development. The programme revealed considerable promise but obviously was totally devoid of scientific adventuring for at least a decade ahead. Sound and steady technical development, linked with a fair measure of caution, seemed to be Munk's policy.

The other two elements of the consortium were more concerned to break new ground from the outset. There were Mr Ken Carline with his company Thermo-Skyships Ltd and Major Malcolm Wren with another company bearing his own name; both companies had policies of picking up where the rigid airship designers of pre-war days had left off. At one stage, a ship approximating to the size of the old *Graf Zeppelin* for the Redcoats Airline of Luton and Gatwick was envisaged, but the airline went out of business and Carline lost his health and had to give up his position.

It was at about this time that technical help came from the far side of the world and thereby introduced a new element of confusion. A new principal designer by the name of Pat Monk arrived from New Zealand and has since made a number of commuting journeys across the globe supervising novel design projects both here and in New Zealand.

So far as the hardware side of the operations is concerned, evidence of activity came to hand in the form of a letter in October, 1982, from Lansdowne Airport in Ohio. The letter was headed *American Skyships Industries Inc.* and was signed by Russell H. Scoville, President & General Manager. This letter declared that "Wren/American Skyships is proceeding with plans to build pressurised, rigid, metal-clad dirigibles . . . in Youngstown, Ohio." There followed further information and illustrations to indicate that a revised version of the type R.30 rigid previously envisaged for Redcoats Airline was now being pursued in America with a form of subsidised assistance from the municipal authorities, who were hoping this would generate employment for residents. One year later it was learned that Russell Scoville had resigned in order to devote more time to his own company, the Financial Assistance Corporation of Youngstown. A letter to American Skyships Inc. to verify the company's future programme has not as yet evoked a reply.

It has been public knowledge for some years that the consortium had considerable backing from European Ferries Ltd., and that it was chaired by their Mr Keith Wickenden. On 9th July, 1983, Mr Wickenden was killed in a flying accident, being succeeded by Andrew Millar. Roger Munk, who may well be considered the founder of the whole enterprise, has been appointed Technical Director.

As we prepare to take our leave of the Cardington scene in 1984, it is indeed a happy thought that we are able to speculate on a future pattern of activity there, far less bleak than might have been expected.

There is little doubt that those cathedrals of Cardington will echo to the song of airship engines for many a year to come.

Appendix 1

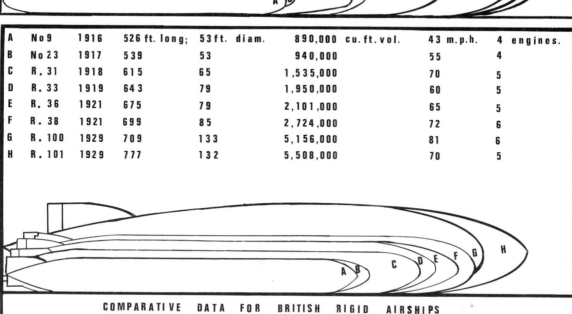

COMPARATIVE DATA FOR GERMAN RIGID AIRSHIPS										
1900 TO 1936										
A	LZ-I	1900	420 ft. long;	39 ft. diam.	400,000 cu.ft.vol.	17 m.p.h.	2 engines.
B	SL-I	1911	432	60	734,500	45	2
C	LZ-24	1914	518	48	800,000	47	3
D	LZ-38	1915	537	61	1,127,000	57	4
E	LZ-62	1916	650	78	1,950,000	62	6
F	LZ-114	1918	743	78	2,419,000	73	6
G	LZ-127	1928	775	100	3,995,000	70	5
H	LZ-129	1936	804	135	7,062,000	83	4

G.A.C. 1/11/80

A	No 9	1916	526 ft. long;	53 ft. diam.	890,000 cu.ft.vol.	43 m.p.h.	4 engines.
B	No 23	1917	539	53	940,000	55	4
C	R.31	1918	615	65	1,535,000	70	5
D	R.33	1919	643	79	1,950,000	60	5
E	R.36	1921	675	79	2,101,000	65	5
F	R.38	1921	699	85	2,724,000	72	6
G	R.100	1929	709	133	5,156,000	81	6
H	R.101	1929	777	132	5,508,000	70	5

COMPARATIVE DATA FOR BRITISH RIGID AIRSHIPS
1916 - 1929

G.A.C. 12-10-80

Appendix 2

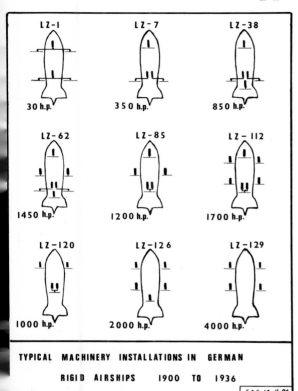

| LZ-1 | LZ-7 | LZ-38 |
| 30 h.p. | 350 h.p. | 850 h.p. |

| LZ-62 | LZ-85 | LZ-112 |
| 1450 h.p. | 1200 h.p. | 1700 h.p. |

| LZ-120 | LZ-126 | LZ-129 |
| 1000 h.p. | 2000 h.p. | 4000 h.p. |

TYPICAL MACHINERY INSTALLATIONS IN GERMAN RIGID AIRSHIPS 1900 TO 1936

G.A.C. 14-11-80

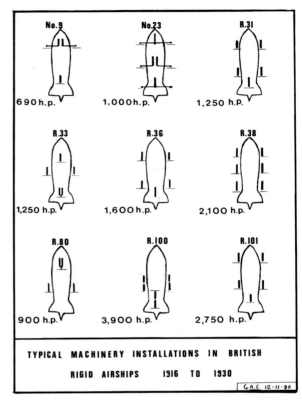

| No.9 | No.23 | R.31 |
| 690 h.p. | 1,000 h.p. | 1,250 h.p. |

| R.33 | R.36 | R.38 |
| 1,250 h.p. | 1,600 h.p. | 2,100 h.p. |

| R.80 | R.100 | R.101 |
| 900 h.p. | 3,900 h.p. | 2,750 h.p. |

TYPICAL MACHINERY INSTALLATIONS IN BRITISH RIGID AIRSHIPS 1916 TO 1930

G.A.C. 12-11-80

Appendix 3

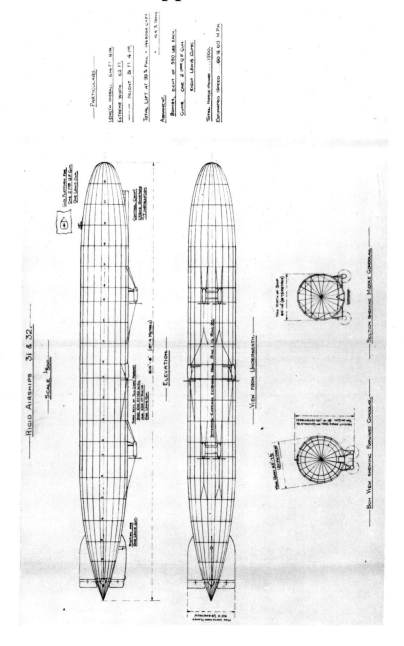

Appendix 4

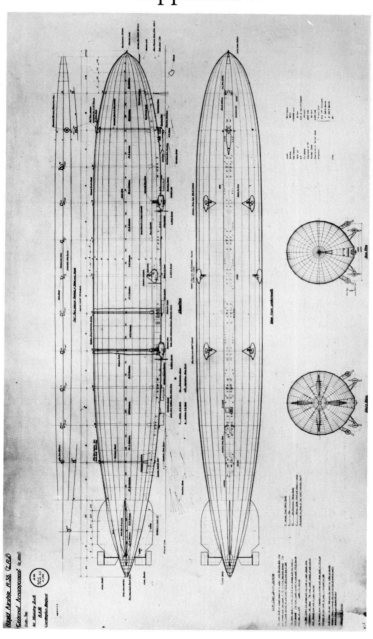

Appendix 5

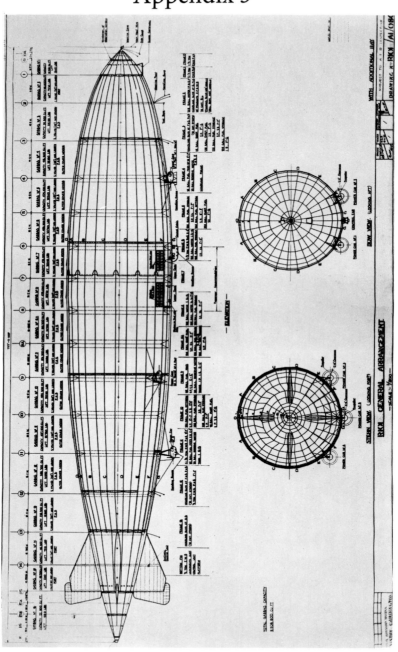

Appendix 6

OFFICERS COMMANDING R.A.F. CARDINGTON

November 23rd, 1936	Group Captain A. A. Thomson, M.C., A.F.C.
February 2nd, 1938	Group Captain G. W. Murus-Green, D.S.O., M.C.
November 8th, 1939	Group Captain A. R. Arnold, D.S.O., D.F.C.
March 21st, 1945	Group Captain H. E. Walker, M.C., D.F.C.
July 4th, 1945	Group Captain R. P. Councel, O.B.E.
March 3rd, 1947	Group Captain J. Bradbury, D.F.C.
April 22nd, 1949	Group Captain J. L. F. Fuller-Good
September 26th, 1949	Group Captain R. A. McMurtrie, D.S.O., D.F.C.
February 25th, 1952	Group Captain S. H. C. Gray, O.B.E.
April 1st, 1952	Group Captain W. H. N. Turner, D.F.C.
May 5th, 1954	Group Captain W. A. Satchell, D.S.O.
July 1st, 1956	Group Captain C. R. Lousada
July 17th, 1959	Group Captain J. H. Kentish, D.F.C.
February 22nd, 1960	Group Captain G. H. Robinson, D.F.C.
March 26th, 1961	Wing Commander P. H. Waterkeyn, O.B.E., D.F.C.
October 28th, 1963	Wing Commander A. R. Scott, D.F.C.
December 29th, 1965	Squadron Leader T. M. Gethings
February 25th, 1966	Wing Commander A. J. Douch
December 5th, 1966	Wing Commander J. Lee, O.B.E.
June 2nd, 1969	Wing Commander F. C. Airey, M.B.E.
March 6th, 1972	Wing Commander G. D. Cooper, M.B.E.
October 4th, 1974	Wing Commander E. W. Lamb, M.V.O.
April 14th, 1976	Wing Commander D. A. R. Matthews
October 26th, 1977	Wing Commander P. Taylor, O.B.E.
October 26th, 1979	Wing Commander A. R. Murray
February 27th, 1981	Wing Commander D. C. Deeble
June 17th, 1983	Wing Commander V. E. G. Patten

Appendix 7

PERSONNEL ABOARD H.M.AIRSHIP R.100 ON ATLANTIC FLIGHTS

Squadron Leader R. S. Booth, A.F.C.	Captain
Squadron Leader E. L. Johnston, O.B.E., A.F.C.	Navigator
Captain G. F. Meager, A.F.C.	First Officer
Flying Officer M. H. Steff	Second Officer
Mr M. A. Giblett, M.Sc.	Met. Officer
Flight Sergeant T. E. Greenstreet	Chief Coxswain
T. Hobbs	Assistant Coxswain
G. E. Long, A.F.M., B.E.M.	Assistant Coxswain
L. A. Moncrieff, B.E.M.	Assistant Coxswain
Angus, W. Y.	Chief Engineer
Atkins, G. K.	Wireless Operator
Ball, R.	Engineer
Broughton, C.	Rigger
Clark, H. W.	Engineer
Cumley, H.	Engineer
Cutts, C. G.	Rigger
Curran, F.	Steward
Deverell, R. L.	Rigger
Disley, A.	Electrician
Flatters, C.	Rigger
Gaye, F.	Engineer
Hodnett, F.	Steward
Hunt, L.	Engineer
Jowett, J.	Engineer
Keeley, S. T.	Ch. Wireless Operator
Lelliott, D.	Engineer
Mann, L.	Engineer Charge-Hand
Millward, H.	Engineer
Meegan, J. F.	Chef
Rumsby, C. H.	Rigger
Savidge, A. H.	Chief Steward
Scott, G. R.	Rigger
Stupple, E. J.	Engineer Charge-Hand
Sturgeon, J. M.	Engineer
Watts, G.	Engineer Charge-Hand
Wiseman, A. F.	Rigger
Williams, F.	Rigger

Wing Commander R. B. Colmore, O.B.E.	Director of Airship Dev't
Major G. H. Scott, C.B.E., A.F.C.	Assistant Director/Flying
Sir Dennistoun Burney	Vickers
Mr N. S. Norway	Vickers
Mr McWade	Aeronautical Inspection Directorate

214

Lieutenant Commander Prentice	Admiralty
Squadron Leader A. H. Wann	Survivor Captain R.38
Mr A. Eldridge	Secretary to D.A.D.

Appendix 8

TECHNICAL PERSONNEL ABOARD H.M. AIRSHIP R.101 OCTOBER 4TH 1930

Flight Lieutenant H. C. Irwin, A.F.C.	Captain
Squadron Leader E. L. Johnston, O.B.E., A.F.C.	Navigator
Lieutenant Commander N. G. Atherstone, A.F.C.	First Officer
Flying Officer M. H. Steff	Second Officer
Mr M. A. Giblett, M.Sc	Met. Officer
Flight Sergeant G. W. Hunt, A.F.M.	Chief Coxswain
Flight Sergeant W. A. Potter	Assistant Coxswain
L. F. Oughton	Assistant Coxswain
C. H. Mason	Assistant Coxswain
Atkins, G. H.	Wireless Operator
Bell, A. V.	Engineer
Binks, J. H.	Engineer
Blake, R.	Engineer
Burton, C. A.	Engineer
Cook, A. J.	Engineer
Church, S.	Rigger
Disley, A.	Electrician
Elliot, F.	Wireless Operator
Fergusson, C. J.	Engineer
Ford, H. E.	Rigger
Foster, P. A.	Rigger
Gent, W. R.	First Engineer
Graham, E. A.	Steward
Hasting, A. C.	Engineer
Hodnett, F.	Steward
Keeley, S. T.	Chief Wireless Operator
Key, T.	Chargehand Engineer
King, W. H.	Engineer
Leech, H. J.	Foreman Engineer
Littlekit, M. F.	Engineer
Megginson, J. W.	Steward
Moule, W.	Engineer
Norcott, A. W. J.	Rigger
Radcliffe, W. G.	Rigger
Rampton, M. G.	Rigger
Richardson, A. J.	Rigger
Rudd, E. G.	Rigger
Savidge, A. H.	Chief Steward
Savory, V.	Engineer

Scott, S. E. .... Chargehand Engineer
Short, G. W. .... Chargehand Engineer
Taylor, C. E. .... Rigger
Watkins, A. H. .... Engineer

Wing Commander R. B. Colmore, O.B.E. .... Director of Airship
                                                      Development
Major G. H. Scott, C.B.E., A.F.C. .... Assistant Director/Flying
Lieutenant Colonel V. C. Richmond, O.B.E. .... Assistant Director/Technical
Squadron Leader F. M. Rope .... Assistant to Assistant
                                                      Director/Technical
Mr A. Bushfield .... Aeronautical Inspection
                                                      Directorate

PASSENGERS ABOARD H.M. AIRSHIP R.101 OCTOBER 4th 1930

Brigadier-General Lord Thomson, P.C., C.B.E., D.S.O. .... Secretary of State for Air
Sir W. Sefton Brancker, K.C.B., A.F.C. .... Director of Civil Aviation
Major P. Bishop, O.B.E. .... Chief Inspector, A.I.D.
Squadron Leader W. Palstra .... Australian Government
                                                      Representative
Squadron Leader W. O'Neill, M.C. .... Deputy Director of Civil
                                                      Aviation, India
Mr James Buck .... Valet to Lord Thomson

Some of the complement of the R.101 on her fatal flight from Cardington. Left to right: Squadron Leader E. L. Johnston, navigator; James Buck, Lord Thomson's valet; Brigadier-General Lord Thomson, Secretary of State for Air; Lieutenant-Colonel V. C. Richmond, Assistant Director of Airship Development; Sir W. Sefton Brancker, Director of Civil Aviation.

Appendix 9

CARDINGTON SHED — CONSTRUCTION DATA

Cardington's first airship shed was constructed during the period from August, 1916, to April, 1917, by A. J. Main and Company of Glasgow and London. It was a steel girder structure with cantilever roof, measuring overall 700 feet in length by 254 feet in width and 145 feet in height. Internal dimensions gave a clear height of 110 feet and a width of 181 feet. The entire building was covered with painted but ungalvanised corrugated sheet iron and both ends had sliding doors covering the full width and height of the structure. Windscreens of a similar style of construction extended from both ends in an attempt to prevent ships being blown against the edges of the doors.

The doors were heavily ballasted and self-supporting; they were moved sideways on multiple flanged-wheel bogies running on rails, the whole double door taking half an hour to open with the power of four capstans turned by teams of strong labourers.

The decision was taken in 1924 to enlarge this shed and to remove one of the sheds from Pulham and re-erect it alongside the first shed at Cardington, enlarging it at the same time in the same manner. The senior engineer in charge was Mr A. R. Gibbs, of the Air Ministry's Directorate of Works and Buildings, the work being carried out by the Cleveland Bridge and Engineering Company of Darlington.

In order to raise the height of the building, it was considered practical to lift the roof bodily with hydraulic jacks, but due to it already being a bolted structure, this proved unnecessary. In the event, the shed was dismantled and the A-frame girders modified on site before being re-erected on correspondingly stronger concrete footings. Lengthening of the shed began by extending the existing railway siding and erecting on it a 7-ton crane with a 140 feet jib which was employed for building a travelling stage 100 feet wide, 80 feet long and 120 feet high and weighing 230 tons. It was built on a double track of 90 feet centres and made to move along the tracks by wire-operated winches. Two 10-ton steam cranes were mounted on the stage and were equipped with 110 feet jibs. With this equipment, the doors were dismantled first and sections lowered to the ground where they were further dismantled before being sent to Darlington for major rebuild. The new doors were of similar type to the old, but being 46 feet higher, demanded an increased width of base and track, the loads on the wheels varying according to wind-strength between 33 and 60 tons per wheel. The present-day doors are electrically powered and weigh 470 tons apiece.

After modification, the shed provided 4¾ acres of unimpeded space, 812 feet by 180 feet with a maximum clear height at the centre of 157 feet; the external overall height being 180 feet. Three internal longitudinal gangways run the length of the roof, access being by three staircases on both sides of the shed and with transverse corridors at high level. The total amount of steel used in each shed was nearly 4,000 tons.

Recommended Further Reading

The War in the Air (6 Volumes), Raleigh & Jones, Clarendon Press (1922 on)

The German Air Raids on Great Britain, Captain J. Morris, Sampson Low (1924)

War on Great Cities, Frank Morison, Faber & Faber (1937)

The Story of a North Sea Air Station, C. F. Snowden Gamble, Oxford University Press (1928), Neville Spearman (1967)

German Rigid Airships (CB 1265), Admiralty War Staff Intelligence, Ordnance Survey (1917)

Zeppelin, Kapitän Hans von Schiller, Kirschbaum Verlag (1966)

My Zeppelins, Doctor Hugo Eckener, Putnam (1958)

Deutsche Luftschiffe 1914–1918, Doctor Otto Dieckerhoff, Druckerie R. Weiss (1973)

The Naval Air Service (Volume 1), Captain S. W. Roskill, Navy Records Society (1969)

The Jellicoe Papers, A. Temple Patterson, Navy Records Society (1968)

The British Rigid Airship 1908–1931, Doctor Robin Higham, G. T. Foulis (1961)

Barnes Wallis, J. E. Morpurgo, Longman (1972)

My Airship Flights, Captain George Meager, William Kimber (1970)

Log of the R.34, Air Commodore E. M. Maitland, Hodder & Stoughton (1920)

Airship, Patrick Abbott, Adams & Dart (1973)

The Zeppelin in Combat, Doctor Douglas Robinson, G. T. Foulis (1962)

The Millionth Chance, James Leasor, Hamish Hamilton (1957)

What About the Airship?, Commander C. E. Rosendahl, Charles Scribner's Sons (1938)

The Goodyear Airships, Zenon Hansen, Airship International Press (1977)

Shenandoah Saga, Thom Hook, Air Show Publishers (1973)

The Airships Akron and Macon, Richard K. Smith, Naval Institute Press (1965)

The Hindenburg Accident (Report No. 11), R. W. Knight, U.S. Government (1938)

The Airmen Who Would Not Die, John G. Fuller, Souvenir Press (1979)

Airship Saga, Lord Ventry, Blandford Press (1982)

The Blimp Book, Hall & Larson, Squarebooks U.S.A. (1977)

Up Ship!, Doctor Douglas Robinson, Naval Institute Press (1982)

The Human Factor, David Beaty, Stein & Day (1969)

Mein Leben fur den Zeppelin (The biography of Albert Sammt), Wolfgang von Zeppelin, Verlag Pestalozzi (1982)

Structural Methods employed by the Schutte-Lanz Airship Company (May 15th 1924), Chief Engineer Gentzcke, Schutte Lanz Holzwerke A.G.

(Published as Technical Memorandum 313 by the National Advisory Committee for Aeronautics in May 1925.) N.A.C.A. (U.S.A.)

Index

Illustrations in bold type

Index of Airships

ERRATUM

The illustration on page 132 is of the control car of the R.100.